Homebuyer Survey to Home Condition Report

Making the Change

Stephen Callaghan
FRICS
FBEng
Dip Arb

Acknowledgements

The author and publishers wish to thank the following for permission to reproduce copyright material:

The 'Home Inspectors Inspection and Reporting Requirements' (formerly known as the Reporting Requirements and Guidance Notes) and the format of the 'Home Condition Report' are © Crown Copyright and reproduced with the kind permission of the Office of the Deputy Prime Minister.

Note: The Home Inspectors Inspection and Reporting Requirements and the Home Condition Report format are under constant review. The content of this publication is based upon the draft of Home Inspectors Inspection and Reporting Requirements available at the time of going to press (January 2006) and will be the subject of further and regular revision as is found necessary.

Energy performance certificates are reproduced with the kind permission of Elmhurst Energy Systems.

Dedications

The helpful comments and advice during the preparation of this book are gratefully acknowledged:

Barry Hall, Ted Richards, Lisbeth Petersen, Barbara Watt, Steve Bull, Peter Hales, Ian Prince, Paul Sparks, Charlie Phayer, Ravi Rihat, Stephen O'Hara of Elmhurst Energy Systems, Christopher Legrand, Simon Nicol, Ian Williams, Ray Simmonds, Gary Reynolds, Tom Littler, Richard Oxley, Stephen Boniface, Andrew Hannan, Paul Latham and Graham Ellis.

Much help and friendly advice was received from James Murphy and James Robinson of RICS Books, for which I am most grateful.

Stephen Callaghan

Published by RICS Business Services Limited
a wholly owned subsidiary of
The Royal Institution of Chartered Surveyors
under the RICS Books imprint
Surveyor Court
Westwood Business Park
Coventry CV4 8JE
UK
www.ricsbooks.com

ISBN 1 84219 246 9

Typeset by Columns Design Ltd, Reading
Printed through Print Solutions Partnership

Contents

Preface

WHY THE HOME CONDITION REPORT?

The professional and business environment of the residential survey and valuation sector is about to change dramatically.

Under sweeping changes contained in the new *Housing Act* 2004, from 2007, sellers will be required to provide a Home Condition Report (HCR) when they place their properties on the market in England and Wales. A voluntary scheme will bring the requirement forward to mid 2006, at which stage at least 7,500 Home Inspectors will be required to service the massive demand.

The impact of the reforms will be drastic as only one in five of home buyers currently has any form of survey carried out. From June 2007, that number will be five in five. Overnight, an industry has been created worth in excess of £1 billion per year.

Homebuyer Survey to Home Condition Report – Making the Change is designed to provide an introduction to a new career as a Licensed Home Inspector, and also to give in-depth advice on how to apply condition ratings in the completion of a Home Condition Report.

WHO CAN THIS BOOK HELP?

This book has been written for anyone aspiring to become a Licensed Home Inspector, as well as those professionals already involved in the preparation of residential building reports. It will be particularly useful to anyone who is in the process of submitting their portfolio of evidence for the Diploma in Home Inspection.

This book is for:

- Home Inspector diploma students;
- chartered surveyors;
- building engineers;
- architects;
- estate agents;
- other building or construction professionals; and
- individuals wanting to explore a career as a Home Inspector.

WHAT ARE THE AIMS OF THIS BOOK?

After reading this book, you will:

- have a clear understanding of the HCR as a new and unique product;
- understand the key differences between the HCR and the Homebuyer Report;
- understand the requirements of the new reporting framework;
- learn how your own existing skills and strengths fit with the new requirements;
- find practical solutions on how to assess condition ratings objectively;
- understand the evolution of the residential survey and valuation marketplace; and
- understand some of the benefits and challenges of home inspection as a career choice.

Foreword

Since the RICS Homebuyer Survey and Valuation (HSV) was launched in 1981, it has undergone several reviews. Today, the service remains widely recognised in the market and is relied on by home buyers across the country.

The HSV was originally intended to set a mid-range survey benchmark, supported by RICS and delivered by its qualified membership. It has become a great success story and many chartered surveyors rely daily on its information as the core of their business.

The *Housing Act* 2004 will bring significant change to the way in which residential properties are bought and sold in England and Wales. Most notably, it will be mandatory from June 2007 for all homes put up for sale to first have a Home Information Pack compiled – a pack that will include the new Home Condition Report (HCR).

In developing the HCR, the government chose to pitch it at the same level as the HSV – which I believe says a lot about the high regard in which the RICS service is held. However, although there are many similarities between the two, the HCR differs in some fundamental respects and it is vital that surveyors and new entrants to the profession, keen to seize this business opportunity, appreciate these.

Hence the need for this guide. I am delighted to recommend it to you with the assurance that RICS will continue to support the HSV for the foreseeable future. It is clear that the landscape for residential surveying services is rapidly changing and the traditional skill set of the qualified surveyor will be in sharp demand. For those embarking on a path towards these new horizons, this guide should provide invaluable support.

Steve Williams
President
Royal Institution of Chartered Surveyors, 2005–6

1 Background to the changes

INTRODUCTION

Currently, most of the information needed by over a million home buyers every year is available to them after they make an offer. What makes the situation even more uncertain and risky for buyers is that only one in five currently commission any sort of survey on the property. A new, clearer, faster and easier way to buy and sell homes is about to be introduced, as the government's home buying reforms take effect. At the centre of the reforms are the Home Condition Report (HCR) and the Home Inspector.

Under sweeping changes contained within Part 5 of the *Housing Act* 2004, from mid-2006, sellers will be encouraged to voluntarily obtain a Home Condition Report (HCR) when they place their properties on the market. New legislation will mean that Home Condition Reports will become mandatory on 1st June 2007, as part of a Home Information Pack (HIP).

Instead of buyers (or solicitors for that matter) commissioning surveyors, from 2007, the seller, estate agent or a HIP provider will commission the new Home Information Pack. The pack is then provided to buyers, giving them key pieces of information to help make an informed decision about whether or not to buy the property.

The *Housing Act* 2004 has created the need for an entirely new profession – the **Licensed Home Inspector**. For experienced surveyors, the Home Condition Report represents a dramatic shift in the way that residential properties are appraised. Importantly for the surveying profession, Home Condition Reports must be carried out by Home Inspectors, and approximately 7,500 Home Inspectors will be needed to cover England and Wales by the time the scheme is launched.

Home Inspectors will be independently certified by an industry-run scheme to be approved by the government. The Home Inspector will be required to demonstrate competence against National Occupational Standards (NOS), for which the Awarding Body for the Built Environment (ABBE) have developed a Vocationally Related Qualification (VRQ) at level 4, which is on a par with a degree. The new award is known as the 'ABBE Diploma in Home Inspection' and was approved in July 2005 by the Qualifications and Curriculum Authority (QCA), and

a number of colleges and universities already offer access to the course. In the longer term, when the new Home Inspector role becomes live, this will become a National Vocational Qualification (NVQ).

Reforming property transactions

The need for wide scale reform of the home buying and selling process has been one of the stated aims of the government for many years, and this was underpinned by research carried out in 1998 by the former Department of Environment, Transport and the Regions (DETR), which showed that:

- The house buying and selling process is the slowest in Europe, with transactions typically taking eight weeks from offer to exchange of contracts.
- Twenty-eight per cent of house sale/purchase transactions fail after an offer has been agreed, at significant cost to the consumer and the industry.
- Of these twenty-eight per cent, about forty-two per cent of failures resulted from the disclosure of defects within the property, emerging either as a result of a mortgage valuation inspection, or a pre-purchase survey (twelve per cent of all sales therefore fail for this reason). The research also showed that these defects were frequently reported to the buyer very late in the transaction process.
- Wastage is very high – the estimated wastage cost to consumers averages £1 million per day.
- It leads to frustration and misery – two in five home buyers and sellers are dissatisfied with the current process, but the research also showed a high level of satisfaction with the professionals involved in the industry generally.

Since 1998, the Office of the Deputy Prime Minister (ODPM) has, together with representatives of the property industry, been undertaking a major study of home buying and selling in the UK. Research has also been undertaken into international comparisons, including Australia, USA and Denmark. Pilot schemes have been set up in Bristol to test the practical operation of Home Information Packs and the robustness of the Home Condition Report, while there has also been consultation on the contents of the HIP and its application in low demand areas.

The research on Home Condition Reports and the Certification Scheme has been undertaken by PIR (formerly SAVA) Ltd., on behalf of the ODPM Home Inspector Certification Board Steering Committee. The stated aims of the reforms are to make the home buying and selling process:

- more transparent – enabling buyers to make better informed offers based upon 'up-front' information that is provided at the beginning of the process rather than near the end;
- more certain – greater certainty within the process provides a less adversarial buying and selling environment;
- faster – reducing the period of time between offer and legal commitment; and
- more consumer friendly – the pack is intended to reduce avoidable and unnecessary time and financial wastage resulting from the high level of failed transactions.

The Home Information Pack

The key documents to be contained within the Home Information Pack are:

- the Home Condition Report;
- an energy performance certificate;
- the basis of the contract, including the terms of sale;
- evidence of title (office copy entries);
- replies to standard searches;
- a seller's property information form;
- warranties and guarantees;
- planning consents, agreements and directions, and building control certificates; and
- additional information for leasehold properties.

The HIP will be required for every residential property that is offered for sale with vacant possession, subject to a number of exceptions that will be defined in detail in the secondary legislation. In general, these exceptions relate to commercial properties, e.g. trading farms, or mixed-use properties such as a shop with a flat above, or properties sold as part of a portfolio of residential investments. Brand new homes will require a HIP, but those constructed under a government approved warranty (e.g. NHBC) are unlikely to require a Home Condition Report.

The duty to assemble a Home Information Pack falls upon the seller, the seller's agent or HIP provider, with copies of the HIP to be provided upon request. Enforcement will be carried out through trading standards officers, as well as the Office of Fair Trading (OFT) and the right of private action.

When the scheme is implemented, there will be a mandatory requirement to include a Home Condition Report (HCR) within the Home Information Pack, and both the inspection and report must be carried out and must be made available before any residential property is placed on the market. The Home Condition Report is the only part of a Home Information Pack not currently supplied during the existing home buying and selling process.

HOME INSPECTORS

Home Inspectors will come from a variety of backgrounds. Initially, the majority are likely to be already working as surveyors and/or valuers, and will be members of professional or trade bodies such as the:

- Royal Institution of Chartered Surveyors (RICS);
- Association of Building Engineers (ABE);
- Chartered Institute of Building (CIOB);
- Institute of Maintenance and Building Management (IMBM);
- Royal Institute of British Architects (RIBA); or
- National Association of Estate Agents (NAEA).

This cohort of potential recruits should have most of the skills and knowledge to undertake Home Condition Reports, but even experienced surveyors will need initial and ongoing training, and continuing professional development (CPD) to meet the exacting requirements of the National Occupational Standards (NOS), which will form the basis of the new qualification.

The principle of 'open access' underpinning the Home Inspector Certification Scheme will mean that literally anyone who wants to apply to become a Home Inspector may do so. The key to the success of the scheme and the quality of Home Inspectors will be the robustness of the assessment regime. As time goes by it is anticipated that the proportion of recruits from related professional areas will grow – and there will of course then develop a third entry route, i.e. that of the school and college leaver without any prior experience. Some of these new entrants will have relevant degrees while others will not.

The approval of RICS membership for credit tariff against the Diploma in Home Inspection was given in the very early stages of ABBE developing the credit tariff framework, and will ensure that RICS members can access a faster-track, experienced-based route to qualification.

CHANGE OF PURPOSE, CHANGE OF STATUS

The Home Condition Report does exactly what it says on the tin!

- It is a report on the condition of a home, intended for consumers.
- It is not a survey in the way we know it, and not merely a defects report.
- It does not contain any reference to value.

Although there are similarities with existing survey products, it is important to recognise that the Home Condition Report will be an entirely new and unique product requiring an entirely new approach. In comparison to other existing survey products, the HCR provides a simpler and more direct form of reporting for consumers, and introduces the concept of **condition ratings**. It may be relied upon by sellers, buyers and mortgage lenders, and because each of these parties has different needs, the Home Condition Report must be expressed in a very objective and impartial way.

It has taken some years to agree the HCR's format, with many stakeholders having been involved, such as the Consumers Association, Council of Mortgage Lenders (CML), RICS, Law Society, Council for Licensed Conveyancers and the National Association of Estate Agents (NAEA). The initial briefing from the former DETR called for a general report on the property, a type similar to the Homebuyer Survey and Valuation (HSV) to give the buyer enough information about the property to enable negotiations to take place. Clearly, the requirements of the report evolved over time and needed to be flexible enough to cater for its widened audience.

It was clear from the original briefing that government ministers were looking for the industry to produce a format that would satisfy a number of key objectives, and be able to:

- focus on condition;
- be consumer friendly;
- keep small print to a minimum;
- include an energy efficiency rating; and
- be produced in a prescribed format that could not be altered.

The working group produced a unique 'mid-range' report, introducing the concept of 'elemental condition categories' as well as narrative. The new report format also had a greater focus on standardised reporting, moving away from subjective or openly opinion-based comment.

At an early stage of development, it was decided that a valuation would not form part of the report. The main drive was to produce a more factual report on the condition of the property, enabling both the buyer and seller to take any factors that would influence agreement as to price into account up front to prevent renegotiation at a later date (normally when surveys and valuations become available). A clear distinction should therefore be drawn between the HCR and other broadly similar survey services, such as building surveys, valuations and HSVs.

The Home Condition Report will be produced electronically via the internet by a Home Inspector, or Home Condition Report Operating Entity using a username, pass code and PIN number to access the system. At this stage, the report will be given a unique reference number and stored electronically.

The existing relationship between surveyors and their clients will undoubtedly change as a result of the introduction of Home Condition Reports. Under the present arrangements, surveyors usually act for one party to the transaction and are specifically commissioned to carry out a survey. More often than not the surveyor is instructed directly by the client (usually the buyer), or through an intermediary such as a lender. The surveyor in such cases typically enters into a standard or bespoke contract with the instructing party. In the current environment where the legal principle of caveat emptor (let the buyer beware) applies, the duty of care between the surveyor and client, together with the wider legal liability is clear-cut. The survey is confidential to the named client.

In the new environment, the HCR is intended to be used and relied upon by a number of unnamed parties — it is a report prepared for consumers. Another important distinction is that everyone marketing a residential property has to have a Home Condition Report, and it has to be in the format prescribed by the legislation. Importantly too, there will be no opportunities for commercial organisations to create hybrid HCR formats.

Does this mean that surveyors need to forget the conventional surveyor/client relationship that they are familiar with? Perhaps not, but certainly a new mind set is required to ensure that any dealings between the Home Inspector, the parties to the transaction and anyone else for that matter are seen to be even-handed and entirely objective. So how do Home Inspectors tread the path between the litigious buyer on the one side and the insulted seller on the other? What is the answer? Home Inspectors must be seen to be:

- fair;
- impartial;
- objective;
- unbiased;
- authoritative; and
- basing their report findings upon factual evidence.

The completed report must reflect a reasonable and balanced view, impartially expressed by the Home Inspector. The condition ratings, justification and comments must appear logical and in a language which is understandable to the buyer, seller and lender.

The provision of a Home Condition Report as part of a Home Information Pack represents a watershed for the property profession and must be viewed in context as just one part of a comprehensive suite of improvement measures that the government has overseen and stimulated. The government intends to dramatically change the home buying and selling process and to bring forward this legislation as part of an integrated reform package and market stimulus that includes initiatives such as electronic conveyancing.

This integrated reform also includes the National Land Information Service (NLIS). Set up in 2001, the NLIS now provides local authority searches, including local land charges, and a range of other services through the holders of channel licences granted by the Lord Chancellor's Department. Local authorities are progressively changing over to electronic delivery of search material and this is having the effect of significantly reducing search times. A good deal of further development work remains to be completed before all local authorities achieve full electronic delivery.

Lenders are also examining more innovative and cost-effective ways of providing themselves with valuation and property risk information in parallel with the traditional mortgage valuation inspection. Examples of this include external 'drive-by' inspections, electronic desktop appraisals and including automated valuation models (also known as AVMs). Lender reforms are also extending to include in-principle mortgage offers, based upon the buyer's credit rating.

'LOCATION, LOCATION, LOCATION' TO 'CONDITION, CONDITION, CONDITION'?

As a result of new technology, changing attitudes to lending and the introduction of the Home Condition Report, the lender's requirement for a full mortgage valuation inspection by a qualified valuer will diminish.

Although most people buying their own home currently do so with the assistance of a mortgage, (a trend which is unlikely to change in the foreseeable future), a number of commentators predict that over the next five years, the requirement for full mortgage valuation inspections is set to decrease by around fifty per cent. In contrast, the introduction of the Home Condition Report will provide a five hundred per cent increase in condition survey work because from 2007, anything between 1.3 million to 2 million HCRs will be commissioned every year. This shift in emphasis will undoubtedly create challenges for the surveying profession and the wider property industry.

Mortgage lenders require valuations to be produced at the lowest possible cost, at the highest possible speed and with the highest possible quality. In order to service this core business requirement, a number of

banks and building societies developed their own in-house teams of valuers and created 'panels' of valuers who would act for them in a consultancy or subcontract capacity. Responding to this need, the large corporate surveying companies, who were able to demonstrate high levels of organisation and quality control, entered the market as key suppliers to the lenders. These types of corporate panel arrangements had the unfortunate knock-on effect that many independent valuers experienced a significant decline in valuation and survey business towards the end of the 1980s and throughout the 1990s.

The *Housing Act* 2004 has provided the property industry with a completely new and level playing field, providing a time of major opportunity for Home Inspectors. In the new environment, it will be the estate agents and HIP providers, and perhaps not the lenders who will be responsible for instructing the Home Inspector. For this reason, the dynamics of the marketplace are likely to change beyond all recognition, and so it becomes increasingly important that the specific marketing focus for Home Inspectors recognises and responds to these changes.

THE SKILLS AND MARKET CHALLENGES

The Home Condition Report is very firmly a product which requires the ability of the Home Inspector to assess condition rather than value. Many existing valuation surveyors will need to sharpen their condition assessment skills and make significant adjustments to their approach to cater for the new HCR product.

For the residential surveying practitioner, the market has until very recently operated in two main segments, consisting of mortgage valuations and condition surveys, with each segment requiring its own specific skills. Most 'level two' valuation surveyors can identify the existence of defects in residential property and are likely to be able to assess their impact on value, but they may not be able to understand the defect's cause or assess the likely cost of repair. On the other hand, 'level three' surveyors (often building surveyors, generally more experienced in construction) are able to assess the cause of defects, the severity and cost of defects, but not necessarily their impact on value.

It could be argued that this skills gap between the two parts of the surveying sector has led to reports which are far from definitive and decisive when it comes to professional opinion. For example, in the context of the Homebuyer Survey and Valuation (HSV), many reports are criticised when surveyors produce long lists of specialist reports for the customer to assemble before they commit to buying the property. This is often referred to colloquially as bringing in 'white van man'

Table 1.1: Comparison of the HSV with the HCR

RICS Homebuyer Survey and Valuation (HSV)	Home Condition Report (HCR)
Valuation included	No valuation included
Free text	'Condition ratings' given for each of the main building elements
Condition reported in the context of effect on value	Factual, objective statements of condition, regardless of effect on value
Repairs form part of the advice	No repair advice
Information provided on location and marketability where this has an impact on value	No information on location or marketability
No requirement to provide energy certificate, although available on some schemes	Energy certificate provided
Many different report hybrids available	Prescribed, mandatory report format
Report produced, often at the eleventh hour, after an offer is made	Report produced before property is marketed
Carried out by a member of the RICS	Carried out by a Licensed Home Inspector
No requirement to act impartially – the surveyor has a duty to act in the best interests of the named client	Requirement on the Home Inspector to act impartially or in other words, to 'act for the Act'
Technical standards contained in the form of practice notes, with some mandatory elements	Detailed technical inspection and reporting requirements, some of which are mandatory
No requirement to demonstrate competence against this product	Competence defined and measured against National Occupational Standards
Intended for one named buyer client in a specific transaction	Intended for consumers
Duty of care to named client only. The contents of the report are confidential to the buyer. Caveat emptor applies	Duty of care to buyer, seller and lender. Caveat emptor (let the buyer beware) still applies
Ethical standards not controlled other than through RICS self-regulatory processes	Reports will be prepared under a strict licensing and quality assurance monitoring regime
Some proprietary software providers, but no standardised electronic delivery of reports	Reports will be delivered electronically, through a secure website
Freestyle text used, with some surveyors opting to use standard caveats and phrases	Report uses 'controlled' mandatory and preferred text
No official policing of scheme, other than via internal quality assurance	Scheme policed by Home Inspector Certification Board
Use of jargon in reports is commonplace	No surveyor jargon
Present voluntary take-up of surveys is only one in five of all home purchases	Statutory requirement under the *Housing Act* 2004 – everyone has to have one
Instructions come via lenders, or direct from the client	Instructions will come from estate agents, HIP providers, or direct from clients

or in contrast, calling for the opinions of a structural engineer to assess the implications of a nasty crack in a wall. In other words, the HSV report often raised a whole series of new unanswered questions, throwing the onus and responsibility onto the buyer to get these questions resolved. The skills gap is partly responsible for this, and so too is the nature of the HSV product. This approach is not sustainable in the future and has no place in a Home Condition Report.

The current survey and valuation business is structured around the requirements of the mortgage lenders. This has led to the predominance of staff surveyor and panel networks principally to service the demand for mortgage-based valuations or surveys. It has also given rise to a valuation-led price structure across the industry. All of these issues have produced tensions and pressures between the corporate and independent surveying sectors. In the HIP

environment, the customers will be HIP providers and estate agents will principally act as facilitators for the home seller.

In the future, the HCR will demand a high degree of condition assessment skills and ability on the part of the Home Inspector to look for defects, and to be able to identify their likely cause and severity. For many would-be Home Inspectors, this will require a good deal of underpinning knowledge in building pathology and construction, together with a commitment to initial and ongoing training to ensure their skills are kept up-to-date.

ENERGY PERFORMANCE CERTIFICATES

The UK government and European Union have for a number of years been involved in examining ways of combating global climate change, particularly in the housing sector. Most people blame the cause of climate change on cars, aeroplanes and power stations, not realising that buildings are the biggest culprit (with homes contributing more greenhouse gases than other buildings).

Buildings account for forty per cent of greenhouse gas emissions and apart from reducing heating costs, increasing the levels of insulation is central to the government's strategy to meet the UK's Kyoto obligations. Specific measures include:

- increasing levels of insulation to those specified by the Building Regulations;
- the Home Energy Efficiency Scheme which provides grants to qualifying households; and
- supplier Energy Efficiency Commitments.

In 1999 a European task group examined ways to reduce energy use in this sector and concluded that 150 million tonnes of carbon dioxide could be saved by 2010. A key recommendation of this work was that a building energy performance directive was required to address the increasing use of energy by buildings. The *Energy Performance of Buildings Directive 2002/91/EC* was formally adopted by the Council of Ministers on 16 December 2002, and is expected to result in savings of 45 million tonnes of carbon dioxide by 2010.

The directive is due to be implemented on 4 January 2006, meaning that anyone selling or letting a home after that date will be required to provide the buyer or lessee with an energy performance certificate, showing the energy efficiency of the building. The certificate will contain an energy label (A-G), similar to the energy labels which are now common on electrical goods.

Despite the draft directive being produced in 2002, awareness of it within the property industry and amongst the general public is poor. The directive on its own will produce a requirement for 5,000 energy surveyors in addition to the 7,500 Home Inspectors needed to service the HCR requirements. It is highly likely that many aspiring Home Inspectors will decide to also become accredited energy surveyors as the first of two phases, so that they are in a position to take full advantage of the demand produced by the directive, which is timed to take effect before the full requirement for HIPs. However, the government can apply for an extension of up to three years if it can show that the industry has insufficient qualified and/or accredited inspectors to prepare the energy performance certificates.

The directive will undoubtedly bring a number of benefits, such as energy savings, brought about by reductions in energy consumption through the focus on improving energy efficiency. Saving energy will help compliance with the emissions targets of the Kyoto Protocol, with the European Union recognising that energy efficiency is the single most cost-effective and publicly acceptable way of meeting our Kyoto objectives.

There is no doubt that this has been one of the key agenda items for the government in backing HIPs and HCRs. The HCR will provide a very effective vehicle to enable the government, over a period of perhaps seven or eight years to have facilitated the assessment of the entire residential housing stock in this country. Turning a government imperative into an industry requirement will clearly have implications so far as costs are concerned.

Approved Standard Assessment Procedure for Energy Efficiency (SAP) ratings are calculated using BRE-approved software. Care must be taken to enter the correct data, or the ratings provided in the report will be inaccurate.

Currently, anyone may calculate a SAP rating using a worksheet that is freely available to all without the need for prior training or qualification. However, this will change in the future when the energy performance certificate will need to be produced using Reduced Data SAP (RdSAP). It is therefore anticipated that the government will set up a quality assurance scheme to ensure that only suitably qualified and independent people carry out RdSAP ratings. In the longer term, it is also planned that surveyors carrying out this work may need to be assessed for competence under a framework of National Occupational Standards (NOS).

The energy performance certificate in the HCR will undoubtedly raise awareness of the energy performance of the property that is placed onto the market. It will allow buyers to easily compare one property with another and provide impartial information on the energy performance, including references to current legal standards. The certificate will be accompanied by recommendations on how to improve the energy performance of the property. Buyers or indeed some sellers may choose to carry out the recommendations. This greater transparency will encourage longer term investment in energy efficiency by enabling potential purchasers to compare buildings in terms of their likely fuel costs and efficiency.

Figure 1.1 shows the first page of an example energy performance certificate. It illustrates:

- an energy efficiency rating, based on the property's energy use and running costs;
- an environmental impact rating, based on the property's carbon dioxide emissions;
- fuel costs, together with total energy consumption per year; and
- potential energy and environmental ratings, if suggested improvements are undertaken.

Section H: Energy Performance Certificate
Save money, improve comfort and help the environment

The following report is based on an inspection carried out for:

Address:
121, Victorian Villas,
Piketown-on-sea,
Pikeshire, MM1 1MN

Building type:	Home
Whole or part:	Whole
Methodology:	RDSAP
Inspection date:	5/12/2005

Certif. Number:

Date issued:

Inspector name:

This home's performance ratings

This home has been inspected and its performance rated in terms of its energy efficiency and environmental impact. This is calculated using the UK Standard Assessment Procedure (SAP) for dwellings which gives you an energy efficiency rating based on fuel cost and an environmental impact rating based on carbon dioxide (CO_2) emissions.

Energy Efficiency Rating

	Current	Potential

Very energy efficient - lower running costs

(92-100) A
(81-91) B
(69-80) C
(55-68) D
(39-54) E
(21-38) F
(1-20) G

Current: 45
Potential: 63

Not energy efficient - higher running costs

UK 2005   Directive 2002/91/EC

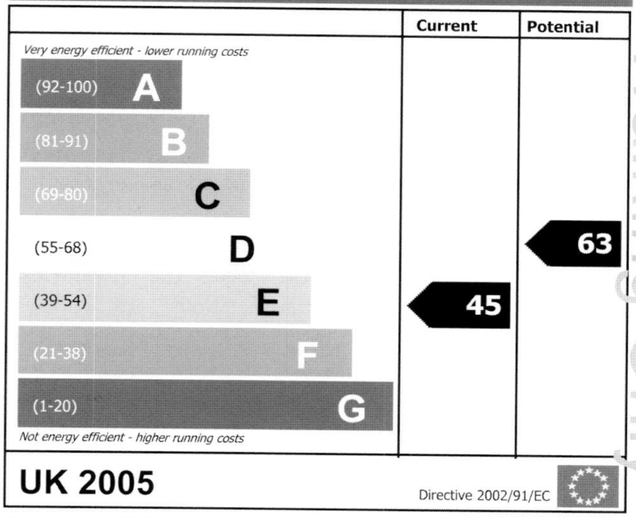

The energy efficiency rating is a measure of the overall efficiency of a home. The higher the rating the more energy efficient the home is and the lower the fuel bills will be.

Environmental Impact Rating

	Current	Potential

Very environmentally friendly - lower CO_2 emissions

(92-100) A
(81-91) B
(69-80) C
(55-68) D
(39-54) E
(21-38) F
(1-20) G

Current: 39
Potential: 58

Not environmentally friendly - higher CO_2 emissions

UK 2005   Directive 2002/91/EC

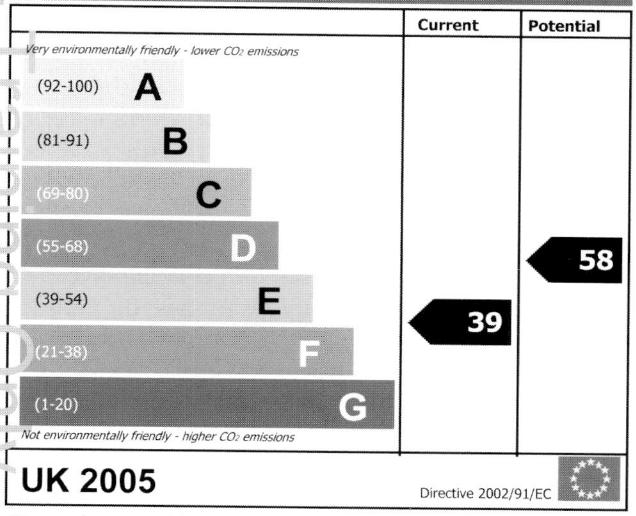

The environmental impact rating is a measure of this home's impact on the environment. The higher the rating the less impact it has on the environment.

Typical fuel costs and carbon dioxide (CO_2) emissions of this home

This table provides you with an indication of how much it will cost to provide lighting, heating and hot water to this home. The fuel costs and carbon dioxide emissions are calculated based on a SAP assessment of the actual energy use that would be needed to deliver the defined level of comfort in this home, using standard occupancy assumptions, which are described on page 4. The energy use includes the energy used in producing and delivering the fuels to this home. The fuel costs only take into account the cost of fuel and not any associated service, maintenance or safety inspection costs. The costs have been provided for guidance only as it is unlikely they will match actual costs for any particular household.

	Current	Potential
Energy use	39,307 kWh/m2 per year	24,269 kWh/m2 per year
Carbon dioxide emissions	7.9 tonnes per year	5.0 tonnes per year
Lighting	£74 per year	£61 per year
Heating	£538 per year	£306 per year
Hot water	£83 per year	£69 per year

To see how this home's performance ratings can be improved please go to page 2

Figure 1.1: Energy performance certificate

Figure 1.2 shows the second page of an energy performance certificate. It illustrates the nature of improvements that might be carried out to improve the energy efficiency of the house and shows the effects of those improvements upon the energy rating. The software automatically produces recommendations and improvements based upon the raw data entered by the Home Inspector, and a target energy rating for the property (achieved by undertaking the recommendations) is also shown.

WHAT IS AN ENERGY RATING?

An energy rating is a way of describing the energy performance of a home that is independent of the size of the home, or how the occupiers use their home. This approach is used to compare homes of different ages, sizes and types on a level playing field, and gives an objective, straightforward indication of the home's standard of energy efficiency.

The energy assessment is currently expressed as a SAP rating – a number between 1 and 120. The higher the number, the better the energy efficiency of the property. It can also be expressed on an A-G scale (similar to the way that electrical appliances are colour coded).

In the current residential surveying industry, a small number of mortgage lenders have a requirement to include a SAP energy rating within their valuation or survey scheme reports. A number of approved energy rating software providers have entered the market, including MVM Consultants, National Energy Services and Elmhurst Energy Systems. None of the existing 'homebuyer report' systems use the full SAP, but use Streamline SAP, RdSAP or something similar.

The RdSAP approach uses smaller data sets to reduce the time taken collecting data in the home. Currently however, the different energy rating software products all use different systems based upon different data sets, and because of the range of data sets, this often produces different results. This current position will not be sustainable when the *Energy Performance of Buildings Directive* and HCR come into force, as they both promote 'a common approach'. Therefore, current energy rating systems will require modification and improvement to ensure that they:

● are sufficiently consistent across software suppliers; and
● comply with the reporting requirements of the energy performance certificate.

Importantly, the energy performance certificate is aimed at promoting the improvement of energy efficiency in buildings and seeks to allow consumers to easily compare one building with another. The certificate must be seen by consumers as providing trustworthy, clear-cut and definitive information that may be fully relied upon.

All three members of The Federation of Assessment Energy Rating Organisations (FAERO), namely MVM Consultants, National Energy Services and Elmhurst Energy Systems, have come together to create the new RdSAP method of providing a condition rating, which is to replace the diverse range of systems which have been used up until now.

Experience from the technical field trials for the RdSAP report show that the additional time required to collect the data needed to produce the energy performance certificate is very little over and above the time required to collect information for the HCR. Although there is no requirement for specialist background knowledge, there is a need for focused training in respect of the energy report. Additionally, for those who may be Streamline SAP accredited, but are not accredited to carry out RdSAP assessments, further top-up training will be required. The training is particularly important in order to become familiar with conventions normally associated with the energy assessment methodology, including:

● construction types;
● shelter factors;
● building measurements; and
● identification of insulation, heating systems and heating controls.

RdSAP inspection and reporting requirements

The following extract is taken from the *Home Inspector Inspection and Reporting Requirements*, which give an overview of the key issues relating to RdSAP assessment and reporting:

'SAP and RdSAP assessment procedures
SAP, the Standard Assessment Procedure, is the Government's approved method of assessing the energy performance of domestic properties. SAP requires the collection of a large amount of data, much of which cannot be obtained from a visual inspection.

The 'Reduced Data Standard Assessment Procedure' (RdSAP) has been developed to assess the energy performance of a domestic property based on a visual inspection of physical details, in order that the Energy Performance Certificate can be incorporated with the HCR (Section H). The RdSAP calculation happens automatically within the software and the 'Energy Performance Certificate' is populated with the required information…

Recording data
Home Inspectors must note and record the specific data required under the RdSAP methodology in a consistent and methodical manner [NOS 4.4.3]. Some of this information will also be part of the general section of

Section H: Energy Performance Certificate

Summary of this home's energy performance related features

The table shows the current performance of each element of this home on the following scale:
Extremely poor/ Very poor/ Poor/ Average/ Good/ Very good/ Excellent

Element	Description	Current performance
Main walls	SO Solid Brick:, Insulation: A As Built, Solid U: 2.10	???
Main roof	P Pitched, Insulation at: J Joists, Thickness: 100 mm	???
Main floor	U: 1.79 A: 57.21 m2	???
Windows	N Normal, Doble Glazed: 0%	???
Main heating	AABC	???
Main heating controls	CBC Program and/or roomstat (NBO)	???
Secondary heating	JAA Efficiency: 50.00%	???
Hot water	HWP From the primary heating system	???
Lighting	Rooms: 7, L.E.L. Fittings: 0, External lights: None	???

Current energy efficiency rating	**E 45**
Current environmental impact rating	**E 39**

Measures to improve this home's performance ratings

The improved energy ratings are cumulative, that is they assume the improvements have been installed in the order that they appear in the table.

Lower cost measures	Typical savings	Energy rating after improvement
Draughtproof all doors and windows	£20	E 46
Solid wall add 50mm (2 inches) insulation	£110	E 54
Sub Total	£130	
Higher cost measures		
Fit thermostatic radiator valves	£23	D 56
Replace boiler with fully controlled gas condensing combi boiler for heating and hot water	£70	D 62
Sub Total	£93	

Potential energy efficiency rating	**D 63**
Potential environmental impact rating	**D 58**

Further measures to achieve even higher standards

Double glaze the single glazed windows	£22	D 63

Enhanced energy efficiency rating	**D 63**
Enhanced environmental impact rating	**D 65**

Improvements to the energy efficiency and environmental impact ratings will usually be in step with each other. However, they can sometimes diverge because reduced energy costs are very occasionally not accompanied by reduced carbon dioxide emissions.

Figure 1.2: Energy performance certificate

the HCR, but Home Inspectors should note the slightly different emphasis required for the RdSAP. For instance, the HCR requires detail of any on-site garage, whereas only attached or integral garages are relevant for the RdSAP....

...The authorised energy rating providers will provide data collection forms consistent with their software.

Over-riding recommendations

The software used for the SAP calculation provides a list of recommended improvements. Home Inspectors must interpret the recommendations and remove those that are inappropriate for the property (for example a recommendation to fill the cavities of a house in an extremely exposed location) [NOS 4.4.4] ... '

© Crown copyright material is reproduced with permission of the Office of the Deputy Prime Minister.

THE PROS AND CONS OF THE NEW PRODUCT

The Home Condition Report forms part of a larger portfolio intended to satisfy the requirements of the *Housing Act* 2004. There is no such thing as a perfect product and it may not answer all the questions that some customers may wish to ask in relation to a particular property.

For the first time, anyone buying a residential property will be enlightened as to its condition, but crucially there are strict limits surrounding the scope of the report. For example, it does not provide:

- speculative comment about the possible condition of elements that could not be inspected;
- information on the severity of defects, repair solutions, or the associated cost; or
- information on issues such as location, marketability or value.

In this sense, the HCR will perhaps pose certain questions, but not necessarily answer all of them.

The HSV has been set as the benchmark for the Home Condition Report. However, the two reports are completely different in that the new HCR service is condition based. The requirement for concise mandatory and preferred text is also likely to dictate the direction that the HCR will take, as this will undoubtedly flavour the tone and emphasis of reports. It is likely to lead to a much more considered, but probably minimalist style of reporting to the extent that providing greater detail in the report would arguably stray into the realms of overstepping the Home Inspector's Terms of Engagement. Many of the more discerning buyers in the marketplace will almost certainly wish to commission their own additional or specialist reports, focusing on aspects not covered in the HCR.

Sellers will become very interested in what the HCR says because the eventual sale price of a home will be affected by its condition and its energy efficiency, but in a way that has never been experienced before. Lenders considering taking the property into mortgage will need to be clear about the structural condition of the building and its general state of repair.

Buyers armed with the HCR will look at two items before deciding on the right offer to make. These are both contained in Section B of the report:

- ***Further Investigation*** (to see if any additional surveys have been recommended); and
- ***Summary of Condition Ratings*** (to see if there are any defects considered serious enough to compromise the property's price).

The HCR has been pitched at the entire home buying and selling public, and will be seen by most as a product that entirely satisfies their requirements. Indeed, first-time buyers entering the property market will be provided, free of charge, with a condition assessment of the home they are about to buy. Compare this with the present scenario in which eighty per cent of all buyers, including those entering the market for the first time, rely entirely upon a mortgage valuation (produced for the lender and not the buyer) when buying their homes.

There is an argument of course, that those who buy only what they are obliged to buy see no benefit in commissioning a condition survey at the present time and may see no benefit in the HCR. However, the poor take-up of surveys could well be caused by the public's mistaken belief that a mortgage valuation *is* a survey. After all, it is usually done by a chartered surveyor! The introduction of the HCR should (finally) put paid to the confusion in the mind of the general public.

A large proportion of buying customers (around seventy-five per cent) who currently commission a survey do so not because they see a benefit in a survey for its own sake, but because they have doubts, and are looking for a guarantee that the property is 'okay'. These customers will find the HCR very useful, and will probably not read the whole report, but skip to the ***Summary of Condition Ratings*** to see whether or not they should be considering buying the particular property. There is generally a high rate of failure for such transactions where the property has several defects because if defects are reported, this type of customer in the present environment may be overcome by doubt and therefore much more likely to pull out. Unfortunately, this type of customer is more likely to sue the surveyor if the least thing is perceived to be wrong with the report. In order to address this, the complaints process surrounding the HCR has been developed to try to overcome spurious claims and complaints. Time will tell whether the arrangements are sufficiently robust to cope with the large volumes of HCRs being produced.

For some people, however, the HCR may not be a complete enough product. For example, it may not be sufficient in scope for those discerning customers buying a country mansion or listed building, who may want more information about outstanding repairs, future maintenance and the associated costs. This type of customer is one of the five per cent of buyers currently commissioning a building survey, rather than a Homebuyer report, which often contains more standard phrases. They are looking for a much greater depth of information about the property so that they can budget for repairs, improvements and future maintenance accordingly, and they are prepared to pay extra for such services. In the future, customers buying large or unusual homes may well decide to appoint a Home Inspector or surveyor directly, irrespective of whether the property comes with a Home Condition Report as standard.

Conversely, these potential shortcomings in the new report should provide the opportunity for Home Inspectors and surveyors to provide a range of complementary and responsive products around the Home Condition Report.

2 The Current Homebuyer Survey and Valuation (HSV)

SUMMARY AND OBJECTIVES OF THE HSV

The current RICS Homebuyer Survey and Valuation was launched in 1997 as the most recent version of a 'mid-range' survey format produced by RICS.

Development of this product took account of market research and the reaction to previous editions dating back to 1981, including written criticisms from several hundred RICS members, four hundred members of the public questioned by telephone, and detailed comments from the Consumers' Association. Seminars and several field tests were also conducted in order to refine the features of the product. As a consequence, the current edition emerged as more client oriented and arguably easier for surveyors to use.

The stated objectives of the HSV are to assist buyers of residential property to:

- make a reasoned and informed judgment on whether or not to proceed with the purchase;
- assess whether or not the property is a reasonable purchase at the agreed price; and
- be clear what decisions and actions should be taken before contracts are exchanged.

The presentation is in the form of a standard pro forma which may be extended with additional sheets if the space provided on the form is insufficient for all the surveyor's comments. This standardisation of approach is an important distinguishing factor between the HSV and a building survey. Building surveys provide ample opportunity for the surveyor to adapt the report format to suit the style of property, but for the HSV this flexibility does not apply.

As the HSV includes a market valuation, it has been adopted in its current form or adapted into very similar 'scheme two' or 'level two' hybrid surveys by several of the large mortgage lenders. This has been a key factor in the wide scale distribution and relative popularity of the service.

Until the middle of 2003, the HSV service was included within the RICS 'Red Book', but this is no longer the case. However, the inclusion of a valuation has required surveyors to adopt a structured approach to the inspection and report, and to take account of factors affecting value, including location, marketability, as well as the property's condition.

In January 2005, following a review of the 1997 Homebuyer Survey and Valuation service, a second edition was published, essentially to rationalise all the existing documentation into the form of Practice Notes and to amalgamate the Scottish version with that for England and Wales.

The current HSV service has also changed status from when it was relaunched in 1997. At the time, procedures were set out in Practice Statement 11 and Annexes A to D of Practice Statement 11 in the RICS 'Red Book'. In 2003, however, following a review of the Red Book, the HSV practice statements were removed.

The purpose of the HSV service adopting a mandatory status was to ensure provision of consistency in the service across the country. Initially applying to England and Wales, its provisions eventually extended to Scottish practice.

Although no clear statistics are available, there is a widely held view that the HSV and its equivalent scheme surveys account for approximately fifteen to twenty per cent of the total available residential survey and valuation market. This is a very low market penetration rate as the greater majority of purchasers at present do not opt to have a survey. This is partly due to a misapprehension that the lender's mortgage valuation (typically carried out by a chartered surveyor) is actually a survey done for them, and so may be relied upon by them.

The objectives of the current edition of the HSV are different from the previous versions, with the main changes summarised in Table 2.1. Whereas previous editions of the HBSV (Home Buyer Survey and Valuation service) provided only facts as the surveyor saw them, the emphasis in the current edition of the HSV shifted to providing not only these facts, but also professional advice based upon them. The advice occupies only a small proportion of the total report, but may well be important to the client. Advice can be found in the following sections of the report:

- in the **Overall Opinion** section at the beginning of the report;
- in paragraphs tagged '**ACTION**', throughout the report; and
- in the **Summary** at the end of the report.

Table 2.1: The development of the RICS Homebuyer Survey and Valuation Service

RICS HSV version (denoted by year)	Objectives
1993	**To provide a concise report on:** • the general condition of the property, (identifying significant defects and repairs essential at the time of inspection; • a brief description of the property; and • any factors likely to materially affect its value.
1997	**To give clients the professional advice which will assist them to:** • make a reasoned and informed judgment on whether or not to proceed with the purchase; • assess whether or not the property is a reasonable purchase at the agreed price; and • be clear what decisions and actions should be taken before contracts are exchanged. **Coverage** The general condition of the property, and particular features which affect its present value and may affect its future marketability. **Focus** What the surveyor judges to be 'urgent or significant matters'.
2005	**To give clients the professional advice which will assist them to:** • make a reasoned and informed judgment on whether or not to proceed with the purchase; • assess at what price it would be reasonable to purchase the property; • be clear what decisions and actions should be taken before contracts are exchanged; and • (in Scotland) be clear about what decisions and actions should be taken before an offer is concluded. **Coverage** The general condition of the property, and particular features which affect its present value and may affect its future resale. **Focus** Matters which the surveyor judges to be urgent and/or significant.

Other major changes of emphasis in the 1997 and 2005 versions were that '*the report focuses on … urgent or significant matters*', with relatively trivial matters to be excluded. The definition of 'significant matters' is given in the description of the service as '*those which, could reasonably be expected in negotiations over price to be reflected in the amount finally agreed*'.

Figure 2.1 shows the current decision path for surveyors carrying out RICS Homebuyer Survey and Valuation Reports. It serves to demonstrate how surveyors currently decide whether or not to report and categorise defects.

THE HSV FORMAT AND STANDARD TERMS OF ENGAGEMENT

The format of the report was completely reconstructed in 1997, as were the Standard Terms of Engagement. The most important change resulted from consumer protection legislation, which required standard terms to be balanced and much clearer.

There was also a need to ensure that clients were aware that alternative survey services were available, and they may have the opportunity to amend the standard HSV service if they so wish – provided, of course, that any such amendment is agreed by the surveyor.

Any amendment must be an agreed addition to (rather than a change in) the concept of the service and must be capable of being reported within the standard format. Additions that the client may want can be provided, but as extra and agreed services. The most common examples of agreed additions have included extensions to the scope of inspection, while the most common extra service is likely to be producing a list of 'minor defects', or arranging for the testing of services.

The inclusion of additions may help with any retrospective assessment of the fairness or reasonableness of the limited service being provided, and could strengthen the argument that the client was under no inducement to agree to the more limited service provided under the standard service.

Minor defects excluded

The standard HSV terms emphasise that '*The report focuses on … urgent or significant matters … Matters which are judged to be not significant or not urgent are generally not included in the report. The surveyor may,*

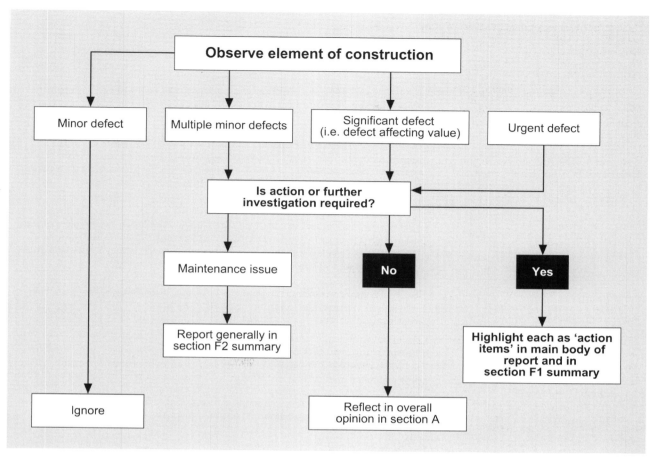

Figure 2.1: HSV decision path

however, comment on any other matters judged to be helpful and constructive.'

In practice, it has been very common for surveyors to overlook such statements of exclusion, often on the principle of self-defence. This often has unfortunate consequences, as where surveyors include some minor defects within a homebuyer report, a court would be entitled to find that they had assumed a more onerous duty to report on all minor defects. On this basis, surveyors could be at risk of being held negligent if they miss one such defect or a series of minor defects.

SUMMARY OF THE HSV SERVICE

Table 2.2 summarises the key features of the existing HSV service and the use of the following categorisations:

- SIGNIFICANT MATTERS;
- URGENT MATTERS;
- ACTION;
- OVERALL OPINION; and the treatment of
- MINOR DEFECTS.

Table 2.2: Summary of the HSV Service

Report categorisation	Contextual meaning of categorisation
SIGNIFICANT MATTERS Significant matters are defined *as 'matters which could reasonably be expected in negotiations over price to be reflected in the amount finally agreed.'* **Location in HSV report** Description of the Homebuyer Service: A3	The definition of 'significant' is very important. It has been imperative to use this word in the report solely as defined. There should be no use of other terms such as major, important, serious, substantial, etc. The word 'typically' qualifies the rest of the definition. Surveyors have had to use their judgment, based on training, experience and local knowledge, in order to interpret its application to each element, based upon circumstances of the case. This includes the prevailing market conditions. A typical negotiation may be taken as one in which the hypothetical parties are average for the type of property and have no unusual attitudes or requirements. It has been essential for surveyors and their clients to have a clear understanding of the matters that may affect the price to be paid, and the use of a single term is aimed to focus their minds on such matters. The word 'significant' is immediately recognisable by the client, but still retains an important element of subjective impression on the part of the surveyor. If a defect or problem is also 'urgent', the urgency has taken precedence over the significance.
URGENT MATTERS Urgent matters are defined as *'defects judged to be an actual or developing threat to the fabric of the building…'.* **Location in HSV report** Section A: *Introduction*	Urgent matters do not have to be, and frequently are not, significant. They comprise those 'essential repairs' normally expected to be covered in a Mortgage Valuation report (including any matter for further investigation), plus any other matters meeting the definition given to the client (in Section A: *Introduction*). A 'developing threat' is one where the first sign of a defect is visible and the surveyor judges that it is likely to develop into an actual threat unless remedial action is taken. All urgent matters reported (regardless of whether they are also significant or not), are listed in headline form in Section F: *Summary*, at F1. All significant (but not urgent) matters are to be listed at F2 or F3.
ACTION The following text is included in the HSV report under Section A: *Action:* *'If, after reading and considering all the information and advice in the Report, you decide to proceed with the purchase, then there are probably some things on which you should take action at once. Each such item is highlighted in the Report with the word ACTION and is also listed in Section F: Summary together with advice on what to do next.'* **Location in HSV report** Section A: *Introduction*	One of the key commitments made to the client at the outset is that each matter on which the client needs to take action at once is highlighted in the Report with the word ACTION and is also listed in Section F: *Summary*. This is easier than it may seem because in practical terms, all urgent matters need action and by the same token, all action matters are urgent. The majority of negligence claims arise from structural instability, roof or infestation problems. Of these, perhaps seventy-five per cent of cases are where the surveyor saw and noted some symptoms, but then failed to properly assess their significance. Perhaps in half of these cases, the surveyor gave advice in the report about the defects, but the advice was not clear about the steps which the client should take. Additionally, that advice did not appear in any summary or recommendations to the client. On this basis, tagging defects in this way is helpful and will help to offset any potential negligence claims.

OVERALL OPINION

The following text is included in the HSV report under Section A: *Overall opinion:*

'Below are my conclusions, in brief, on the price at which it would be reasonable to purchase the Property, and on particular features which affect its present value and may affect its future resale. The opinion takes no account of factors outside the scope of the HOMEBUYER Service.

It is hoped that this overall view will help you to keep in perspective the detailed facts and advice which follow. You are asked to bear in mind particularly that it can be misleading to treat individual matters in isolation. So that you may use this Report to best advantage in reaching your decision on whether or not to proceed with the purchase of this Property, *you are most strongly advised to read and consider its contents as a whole*.'

Location in HSV report
Section A: *Introduction*

Undoubtedly, the *Overall Opinion* section of the report has caused the greatest confusion to practitioners and in particular, its location at the start of the report.

The Overall Opinion serves as a signpost, and opening 'headline' to the main report, while the *Summary* serves as a closing action programme.

The Overall Opinion is the surveyor's professional and concise opinion of:
- the price at which it would be reasonable to purchase the property; and
- its resale prospects; plus
- brief mention of main features and/or disrepair affecting the above.

The Overall Opinion does not contain:
- checklists;
- a description of the property; or
- an opinion of whether or not the surveyor themselves would buy the property.

The Summary is a checklist of matters raised previously in the report, including:
- ACTION points (in headline form); and
- other significant matters; plus
- advice on how to take any action recommended.

The Summary does not contain any:
- new information;
- additional descriptions;
- opinion of condition;
- opinion of value; or
- comment on purchase price.

MINOR DEFECTS

'Matters assessed as not urgent or not significant are outside the scope of the Homebuyer Service and are generally not reported. However, other matters which may be of concern are reported where the Surveyor judges this to be helpful and constructive.'

Location in HSV report
Description of the Homebuyer Service: C2

Reporting on miscellaneous minor defects which do not genuinely fit within these criteria is not part of the service. Where surveyors include minor defects within the Homebuyer report, the courts would be entitled to find that they had assumed a more onerous duty to report on all minor defects.

While limiting the scope of the standard service, the description at C2 does not prevent clients from having any additional service which they may want and are willing to pay for. However, those many clients who want nothing extra, will pay nothing extra.

The value of including agreed additions to the service is that the client is informed that the specified additions are not included in the service. The inclusion of additions also helps with any assessment of the fairness or reasonableness of the limited service being provided, and should strengthen the argument that the client had no inducement to agree to the more limited service provided under the standard service.

Whether or not surveyors choose to offer any such additional services is a matter of personal choice. The only constraint is that they must not be linked to the Homebuyer report, but they must be agreed, reported upon and invoiced separately from the HSV commission.

Surveyors are under an obligation to tell the client what additions to the standard service (and/or what extra services) they are prepared to provide, and (where relevant) to ensure that the distinction is understood.

3 The Home Condition Report

The HCR is unique – it is the end product of considerable industry research and development.
It will not be a full building survey and essentially, it is pitched as a 'level two' inspection, based on a non-invasive and visual inspection that provides a snapshot of the property's condition on the date of inspection.

SUMMARY OF THE NEW HCR SERVICE

The HCR is intended to occupy the mid-ground between a market valuation type inspection (known as level one), and a building survey (level three). In some ways the HCR is therefore pitched at the same level as the RICS Homebuyer Survey and Valuation (HSV), except it does not contain a valuation. However, it is important to appreciate that the HCR is not the HSV under another name, as new skills are required to fulfil the requirements of the new service.

The HCR has a number of innovative key features:

- reports will be in a prescribed, standardised format, with the intention that it is flexible enough to be used for any style and type of property from studio flats to large mansions;
- reports will be delivered electronically, through a secure web framework;
- reports will be prepared under a strict licensing and quality assurance regime;
- it has been designed to be consumer friendly, consistent in its presentation and transparent in what it offers;
- it introduces the concept of 'condition ratings', intended to help buyers focus on the key issues relating to the property's condition; and
- it should be free of unnecessary technical jargon, use plain language and 'controlled' text wherever possible.

Home Inspector Inspection and Reporting Requirements

The *Home Inspector Inspection and Reporting Requirements* (presently in draft form) will provide guidance and assist Home Inspectors to produce Home Condition Reports in accordance with the requirements of the *Housing Act* 2004 and the National Occupational Standards (NOS) for Home Inspectors.

The *Home Inspector Inspection and Reporting Requirements* are arranged in two parts:

- Part I provides explanations and examples for the application of the NOS in practice.
- Part II concentrates on the technical aspects in the production of the HCR, demonstrating the practical application of Home Inspectors' knowledge, and experience of building construction and pathology.

Appendix B contains extracts from the *Home Inspector Inspection and Reporting Requirements*, which help provide an insight into the new HCR service.

THE HOME CONDITION REPORT PRESCRIBED FORMAT

The format of the Home Condition Report is broken down into the following sections:

The role of the Home Inspector and the home condition report;

A. General Information;
B. Summary;
C. Conveyancing and Health & Safety Issues;
D. Outside Condition;
E. Inside Condition;
F. Services;
G. Grounds; and
H. Energy Performance Certificate.

The contents of each individual report section are summarised below.

The role of the home inspector and the home condition report

As well as providing a preamble to the report itself, the terms on which the report is prepared are also contained within this section, and these correspond with those that have been sent previously to the seller with the 'Confirmation of Instructions' letter. The extent of inspection and the scope of the service are set out in layman's terms, describing those parts of the property that are included and those that are outside the service requirements. The simplicity of language is intended to reduce the potential for misunderstanding, and includes the following headings:

- Role of the Home Inspector and the Home Condition Report;
- Introduction and terms on which the report is prepared;
- What this report tells you;
- What this report does not tell you;
- What is inspected; and
- Definition of condition ratings.

Section A – General Information

This section contains general information relevant to the property being inspected, including the following:

- Full address of the property;
- Property reference number;
- Home Inspector details;
- Company details;
- Report reference number;
- The number of HCRs done on this property in the last twelve months; and
- Disclosure on related parties.

Section B – Summary

This section builds upon the general introductory information contained in Section A and includes:

- date of inspection;
- weather conditions;
- whether the property is furnished/unfurnished;
- date of original construction;
- name and date of any extension;
- date of conversion, if appropriate;
- type of property;
- signs of tenancy occupation;
- whether the property is located in a predominantly tenanted area;
- whether the property is located in a conservation area or likely to be listed;
- general information for flats/maisonettes;
- accommodation (number of storeys and rooms);
- gross external floor area;
- reinstatement cost for insurance purposes;
- nature of commercial uses in the block;
- a short general description of the construction (roof and walls, floors and windows);
- details if the property is of system built construction;
- mains services;
- central heating;

- outside facilities, e.g. garage, gardens, permanent outbuildings;
- roads and footpaths;
- summary of overall condition of the property;
- widespread defects that affect multiple parts of the property;
- summary of structural movement;
- items for further investigation; and
- summary of ratings (automatically generated by the report software itself).

Section C – Conveyancing and Health & Safety Issues

Separated into three parts, this section deals with:

- Issues for conveyancers;
- Dangerous materials and contaminated land, subsidence and flooding; and
- Health and safety risks.

Within Section C, the Home Inspector is required to identify matters that need further consideration or investigation by the conveyancer, including (but not limited to) matters such as highway adoption, sewers and drains, water supply, rights of way, covenants, easements and rights, planning and statutory consents, freehold owner consents, flying freehold, environmental concerns, mining, undefined boundaries, general legal risks, previous structural works, guarantees, new build warranties, insurance claims outstanding, contamination, flooding, Tree Preservation Orders, etc.

The Home Inspector is also required to report upon any health and safety risks considered to affect the property. These are from a prescribed list, comprising:

- Inadequate provision for escape from windows increasing risk in event of fire;
- Inadequate precautions to control the spread of fire between the garage and the dwelling;
- The lack of fire doors;
- The lack of safety glass;
- Property located in a high risk radon gas area;
- Unguarded roof terrace;
- Unusually steep staircase;
- Lack of handrail on the staircase;
- Smell of gas in or around the property;
- Loose, or unsafe elements of the building, e.g. tiles, TV aerials, parapets; and/or
- Inappropriate use of part of the building as living accommodation.

Sections D to F

Section D – Outside condition, Section E – Inside condition and Section F – Services, comprise the parts of the report which are devoted to condition. When completing Sections D, E and F, the Home Inspector is required to describe individual elements, along with comments on condition and justification for the rating given. Table 3.1 includes the individual elements of a property within sections D to F that need to be addressed individually and given a condition rating.

Section G – Grounds

The Home Inspector is required to report the overall condition of garages, permanent sheds, permanent outbuildings, boundary and other walls, paved areas, shared facilities, detached conservatories and other structures in general terms, but is not required to provide each element with a condition rating.

Section H – Energy performance certificate

The Energy Performance Certificate provides the property with a Reduced Data Standard Assessment Procedure (RdSAP) rating in line with the European *Energy Performance of Buildings Directive* 2002/91/EC and global commitments to reduce carbon dioxide emissions.

The RdSAP rating is calculated by one of the government licensed and approved energy rating software organisations. The software is designed to generate general recommendations towards improvements that may be undertaken to help improve a property's energy efficiency rating. The recommendations are also included within the energy performance certificate, along with their projected savings on energy costs.

In order that this may be achieved, the Home Inspector is required to collect appropriate data on site, e.g. floor areas, construction type, nature of any heating systems, and general levels of insulation. Table 3.2 provides a range of datasets and the appropriate corresponding data that is required for completion of an energy performance certificate.

Report sign off

The final section of the report is the Home Inspector sign off, which requires the following details about the Home Inspector, including:

- name and address;
- contact details;
- qualifications;
- Home Inspector's licence number;
- date of report;
- facsimile signature of Home Inspector (taken from the database); together with
- appendix to the Terms and Conditions of a Home Inspector, containing information relating to complaints procedures.

GENERATING A COMPLETE HCR

Completed reports will be delivered electronically from a secure and password protected website after the Home Inspector has inputted all the necessary data within the report writing software.

The basic report template is twenty pages long, but is in a flexible format to cater for a variety of different property types.

The report format is copyrighted and cannot be used by the general public. After completion of the report's research and development work, it will become available via licensed Home Inspectors only. A licensed Home Inspector is one who has attained the required NOS for Home Inspectors, and holds a valid Home Inspector's Licence.

Once appointed to carry out the HCR, preliminary investigations may need to be undertaken by the Home Inspector, such as a desktop exercise which may consist of historical or background documents made available by the named client, pack provider, legal adviser or agent. This stage of the process may occur before or after the inspection, but often provides information critical to the inspection findings. Research may be undertaken through third parties, such as local

Table 3.1 Breakdown of individual elements requiring a condition rating

Section D – Outside condition (Individual elements)	Section E – Inside condition (Individual elements)	Section F – Services (Individual elements)
D1 Chimney stacks	E1 Roof structure	F1 Electricity
D2 Roof coverings	E2 Ceilings	F2 Gas/Oil
D3 Rain water pipes and gutters	E3 Internal walls, partitions & plasterwork	F3 Water
D4 Main walls and claddings	E4 Floors	F4 Heating
D5 Windows	E5 Fireplaces and chimney breasts (and the outside of flues)	F5 Drainage
D6 External doors	E6 Built-in fittings	
D7 All other woodwork	E7 Inside woodwork	
D8 Outside decoration	E8 Bathroom fittings	
D9 Other outside detail	E9 Dampness	
	E10 Other Issues	

Table 3.2: Data requirements for completing Section H of the HCR (energy performance certificate)

Data category	Data required
Property type	<ul><li>Property type (e.g. bungalow/detached)</li><li>Number of storeys</li><li>Date of construction</li></ul>
External perimeter	External walls perimeter (in linear metres)
External floor areas	External floor area (in metres squared)
Average storey height	Average storey height (in metres)
External wall type	<ul><li>Wall types for main, secondary and tertiary walls (e.g. Cavity uninsulated)</li><li>Main wall thickness (in millimetres)</li></ul>
Roof type and ground floor type	<ul><li>Roof insulation thickness for main and any secondary roofs (in millimetres)</li><li>Ground/lower floor type (e.g. Solid uninsulated)</li></ul>
Doors, windows and open fires	<ul><li>Number of external doors</li><li>Percentage of windows double-glazed</li><li>Percentage of openings with draught proofing</li><li>Number of open fireplaces</li></ul>
Space and water heating	<ul><li>Main heating type (e.g. Gas Floor mount)</li><li>Heating control type (e.g. Programmer, room stat & thermostatic radiator valves)</li><li>Secondary heating type (if present)</li><li>Water heating type</li><li>Whether underfloor heating is present</li></ul>
Hot water cylinder and electricity tariff	<ul><li>Type of hot water cylinder</li><li>Type of cylinder insulation and thickness of insulation (if relevant)</li><li>Type of electricity tariff (e.g. Standard)</li></ul>

authorities, or by reference to published information, such as geological maps. Investigations should be regarded as supplementary to the Home Inspector's working knowledge of the property in question.

The *Home Inspector Inspection and Reporting Requirements* do not specify inspection times for properties. It is likely that a typical three bedroom, two reception room house of around ninety to one hundred square metres should usually take between around seventy-five minutes to two hours to inspect.

There is no prescribed sequence for the HCR inspection and it is purely a matter of personal preference. The process can vary and may even be dictated by the weather conditions at the time, but most Home Inspectors are likely to begin with a friendly introductory conversation with the home owner, at which stage a number of searching and probing questions regarding the property are asked. Typical questions to ask the home owner or agent before an inspection are included in Table 3.3. and the second page of the site notes in Appendix D (page 130).

A reasonably rapid walk through the whole building provides a general overview for the Home Inspector, before beginning the in-depth inspection. There are three key elements to be included in any HCR inspection, illustrated in Figure 3.1.

A systematic inspection not only saves wasted time, but it goes a long way towards reducing the risk of missing important defects. The objective here is to have a logical sequence of inspection that can be used routinely in order to:

- minimise the risk of omissions;
- keep time spent inspecting to a reasonable level; and
- enable objectivity in the report.

All parts of the property should be surveyed as far as practically possible, and reasonable trails of enquiry should be followed, provided that the inspection remains 'non-invasive' and visual.

Table 3.3: Questions to ask a seller prior to inspection

- What is the **age** of the property?
- What is the **tenure** of the property?
- If the tenure is leasehold – how many **years until expiry**?
- Have any **previous alterations, extensions or other works** been carried out?
- **How long** have you owned/leased the property?
- Is the property **listed**, and if so, at what **grade**?
- Is the property located within a **conservation area**?
- Has the property or immediate locality been affected by **flooding**?
- Are there any **rights of way** that affect the property?
- Have any **structural repairs** been carried out? (E.g. underpinning or structural strengthening?)
- Do you have any **guarantees** or **warranties** that affect the property?
- What **mains services** are currently connected?
- What is the **boiler age** and service history?
- Where is the **stopcock** located?
- Are the **roads** adopted, unadopted or private?
- Are you aware of any **disputes, covenants or restrictions** affecting the property?

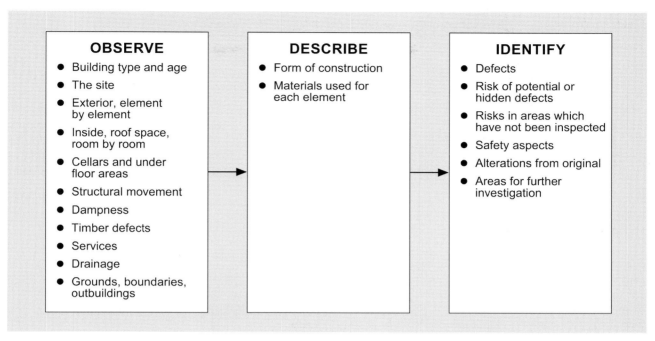

OBSERVE	DESCRIBE	IDENTIFY
• Building type and age • The site • Exterior, element by element • Inside, roof space, room by room • Cellars and under floor areas • Structural movement • Dampness • Timber defects • Services • Drainage • Grounds, boundaries, outbuildings	• Form of construction • Materials used for each element	• Defects • Risk of potential or hidden defects • Risks in areas which have not been inspected • Safety aspects • Alterations from original • Areas for further investigation

Figure 3.1: Key elements for a HCR inspection

For areas of the building that are locked or secured, such as a loft hatch that has been screwed shut, it may not be possible to make any meaningful comment about any such areas that have not been inspected. Additionally, a report containing many references to areas or elements 'Not Inspected', may fall short of consumer expectations. For these reasons, it would be appropriate wherever possible to ask the home owner to open any locked rooms or access hatches to enable a more complete inspection to be made.

Making an accurate and legible record of the inspection is essential. Queries can be raised several months or years after the case is closed and it gives an unprofessional impression if site notes or computer records of the inspection are unavailable. Indeed, mounting a defence to a negligence claim often relies upon a complete set of site notes, or records made of contract discussions. Such notes therefore form a retrospective record of conduct and behaviour, and will represent prima facie evidence of the Home Inspector's competence.

Some Home Inspectors will hand-write notes, some will capture data using sophisticated personal computer systems, and others will choose to dictate their notes during an inspection and word process them afterwards. Any method would satisfy the requirements of the *Home Inspector Inspection and Reporting Requirements*, but simply dictating the report on-site, without making notes would not be acceptable as this would not allow the Home Inspector sufficient time for reflective thought.

The use of pre-printed forms or checklists are strongly recommended as a method of demonstrating a systematic means of gathering and recording evidence arising from the inspection. A home inspection site notes template is included in Appendix D.

CONDITION RATINGS AND THEIR APPLICATION

The primary purpose of condition ratings is to help sellers and prospective buyers focus their attention on the most serious or urgent defects affecting the property before a price is agreed and a formal commitment to purchase is entered into. An example condition rating exercise is included in Appendix C.

Condition ratings enable a quick and simple method of comparing defects on one property against another, and are part of the government's requirement for the HCR to be as user friendly and transparent as possible. This will assist potential buyers during an initial review of properties on the market, or immediately prior to making an offer. The HCR is quite explicit in focusing attention on building elements with a category three condition rating and therefore, should assist in flagging up the need for repairs to the property in a graded way.

The report should assist sellers and estate agents to set realistic prices and provide the opportunity for sellers to carry out any necessary repairs before offering their property for sale. Since the vast majority of sellers are also buyers, it is likely that any additional cost will be balanced by savings on the purchase.

Sellers, buyers and mortgage lenders will be entitled to rely upon the HCR. Table 3.4 shows the condition ratings as they are defined in the Terms of Engagement.

Table 3.4: Definitions of HCR condition ratings

Condition rating	Definition
Rating 1	Satisfactory condition. No repair is presently required. Normal maintenance must be undertaken.
Rating 2	Repairs are required but the Home Inspector does not consider these to be either serious or urgent.
Rating 3	Defects of a serious nature or defects requiring urgent repair.

ASSESSING AND RATING ELEMENTS FOR THE HOME CONDITION REPORT

Assessing the condition of key elements of a residential property and applying a condition rating will require the skill and judgment of an appropriately trained and experienced Home Inspector. The HCR provides clear definitions for each of the three condition ratings. Figure 3.2 shows the simple condition rating process, taking into account broad categories of condition.

Condition rating one

The HCR defines condition rating one as:

'Satisfactory condition. No repair is presently required. Normal maintenance must be undertaken.'

This rating should be applied where there are no indications of present or potential defects that require the undertaking of a specific repair in the foreseeable future. The undertaking of normal maintenance as part of a planned programme is not treated as a repair for the purpose of the HCR.

Use condition rating one where there is:

- no indication of a defect;
- nothing to lead to a potential defect; or
- no specific repair required.

The need for normal routine maintenance, or a shortcoming or deficiency in an element or part of the building are not treated as repairs in the context of the HCR.

Applying this condition rating to a building element is effectively giving it a 'green light'.

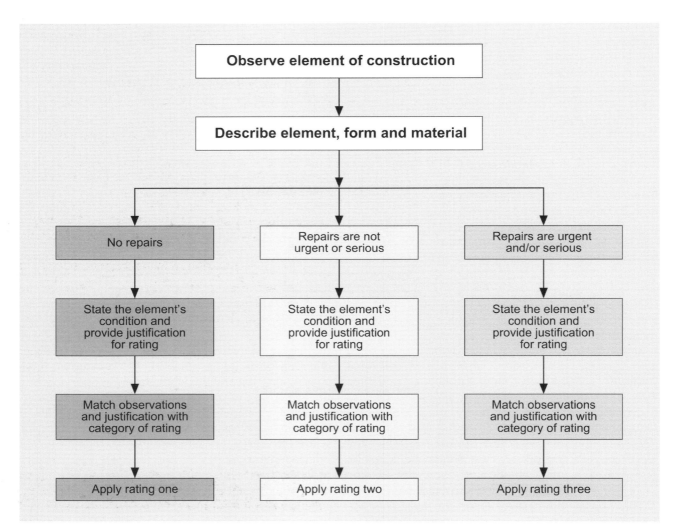

Figure 3.2: The condition rating process

Condition rating two

The HCR defines condition rating two as:

'Repairs are required but the Home Inspector does not consider these to be either serious or urgent.'

This rating is to be applied where repairs are required, but there is no immediacy about them, and if they are not of a serious nature. Any required repairs that may lead to material deterioration or damage to the structure of the property if not undertaken quickly, are not appropriate in this category.

Use condition rating two where:

- a repair is required; and/or
- there is minimal risk of the defect developing into a serious defect.

It is also important to bear in mind that 'condition rating two' repairs may accompany normal maintenance requirements for the building.

Condition rating three

The HCR defines condition rating three as:

'Defects of a serious nature exist or require urgent repair.'

This rating is appropriate where the Home Inspector considers that there is a need for immediate repair work or where the defect is an actual or developing threat to the fabric of the building. It should be used where, for example, any of the following apply to the defect:

- it may compromise the structural integrity of the property; and/or
- it may spoil the intended function of the building element; and/or
- it will affect the health or safety of the occupier; and/or
- it may have a high cost associated with it.

A category three condition rating can also be applied where:

- the failure to speedily repair or rectify a defect (however small), could lead to deterioration of the fabric or structure of the property;
- there is a serious health and safety risk (which might or might not require further investigation); or
- there is a serious defect which requires further investigation.

Not Inspected

This 'rating' is to be shown when any particular element of the property was not inspected, due to there being no access available.

The following is an extract taken from the Home Inspector Inspection and Reporting Requirements, highlighting the approach to be taken in relation to the application of condition ratings:

'Assessment of individual Condition Ratings is a matter for Home Inspectors' professional judgement. They should:

- *refer to condition only, not reflect purely cosmetic issues that have no effect on longevity or performance*
- *take into consideration the cost of repair*
- *reflect any detrimental effect on surrounding building elements*
- *reflect performance*
- *compare 'like with like', e.g. don't compare the life expectancy of a flat felted roof with a pitched, tiled one*
- *assume that regular maintenance will be undertaken in future*
- *be consistent*
- *follow generally accepted building practice*
- *be reasonable – perfection is not the norm*
- *not reflect differences in product quality unless performance and life expectancy are seriously impaired*
- *disregard individual taste or fashion.*
- *Home Inspectors must be factual whenever possible, and indicate in the 'Justification' box in Sections D, E and F of the HCR when making assumptions or expressing opinions based on professional experience and knowledge. For instance, if there are signs of an active dry rot attack that is a fact; its extent and severity will usually be an assumption.'*

© Crown copyright material is reproduced with permission of the Office of the Deputy Prime Minister.

REPORTING DEFECTS: WHAT TO REPORT AND WHERE TO REPORT IT

Table 3.5 includes some of the key factors to be taken into account in determining an appropriate condition rating.

An example condition rating exercise is included in Appendix C.

THE THREE STEPS TO REPORTING

Against each element within Sections D, E and F of the Home Condition Report, you need to follow the 'three steps to reporting':

1. **DESCRIBE ELEMENT, FORM AND MATERIAL**
2. **DESCRIBE CONDITION AND JUSTIFICATION**
3. **MATCH JUSTIFICATION TO RATING**

If you find a defect you should report it within the primary element which contains the source of the problem. For example, damp penetration due to water

Table 3.5: Determining an appropriate condition rating

Building element	Routine inspection process	Typical characteristics
Chimney stacks	• Viewed from various points within the property boundaries and from adjacent public areas if necessary • Close-up inspection often impossible from ground level • Binoculars often need to be used • Often impossible to verify plumbness and stability without closer examination • Follow any trails of suspicion internally	• Often high and difficult to reach • Exposed to all weathers • Often unstable structures • May have been neglected throughout the life of the building • Defects very likely to cause damp penetration • Damp may lead to timber defects
Roofs and roof structures	• Viewed from various points within the property boundaries and from adjacent public areas if necessary • Close-up inspection often impossible from ground level • Binoculars often need to be used • Flat roof surfaces (not more than three metres above ground level) viewed from safely positioned ladder • Flat roof areas not walked upon • Often impossible to verify roof gradients and weather tightness without closer examination • Follow any trails of suspicion internally	• Often high and difficult to reach • Provides primary protection function for the whole building • Any defect is very likely to affect other internal elements • Defects such as loose tiles may pose a health and safety threat that needs to be reported in the HCR
Walls	• Viewed from various points within the property boundaries and from adjacent public areas if necessary • Close-up inspection often possible from ground level, unless concealed by climbing plants, etc. • Binoculars often need to be used for upper storeys of tall buildings • Search thoroughly for the effects of structural movement, including crack damage, bulging, bowing, tilt, loss of serviceability • Check for general plumbness of walls with a spirit level • Follow any trails of suspicion internally	• Often provide the main structural support to the roof and floors • Protect the fabric of the building from extremes of weather and noise • Condition may be concealed from view by cladding, render and vegetation • A key indicator for structural movement within the building as a whole
Windows, doors and joinery	• Viewed from various points within the property boundaries and from adjacent public areas if necessary • Close-up inspection often possible from ground level, unless concealed by climbing plants, etc. • Binoculars often need to be used for upper storeys of tall buildings • Check for general cambering of cills/thresholds with a spirit level • Follow any trails of suspicion internally	• Often have a short life expectancy • Often prone to rot or deterioration • Sealed unit double glazing prone to misting • Have many functions, including escape in the event of fire or other emergency • Intended to provide security • Vulnerable to poor DIY repairs
Damp (and timber defects)	• Thorough search for dampness, including the use of an electronic damp meter • The most likely cause of any damp should be determined wherever possible • Representative check of timberwork in vulnerable areas, e.g. loft, understairs cupboards, and any areas of flooring that are accessible (without removing carpets or floor coverings) • Requirement to follow reasonable trails of suspicion	• Penetrating and rising damp • Bridged, absent or defective damp proof course • Leaking plumbing and appliances • Poor ventilation to sub-floors • Rot and wood boring beetle infestation • Condensation often a problem
Services	• No 'tests' are carried out • A visual inspection • Checked for 'normal operation' • If turned 'off', they will not be turned 'on' by the Home Inspector • Drain covers will be lifted if accessible and safe to do so • Lack of ventilation to gas boilers • Requirement to follow reasonable trails of suspicion	• Blockages and damage to underground drains • Blocked gulleys and soakaways • Aged electrical cabling and fittings • Lack of protective devices causing a health and safety risk • Badly sited boilers and flue outlets • Leaking tanks and radiators • Poor installation • Vulnerable to DIY repairs (any such repairs to services are likely to arouse suspicion)

ingress because of a faulty chimney flashing, should be reported under *D1 Chimney stacks*.

A full description of the problem should be given in relation to the building element. The description should stick purely to the facts and include the approximate location of the defect (e.g. upper, lower, right-hand side, left-hand side, rear or front chimney stack).

Consequential damage to other parts of the building should also be mentioned under the primary element. For example, '*The weatherproofing between the chimney stack and the roof is missing, causing damp penetration. This is considered serious and in need of urgent repair or replacement.*'

The condition rating associated with the defect should take account of the work needed to rectify the primary building element, together with work needed to repair consequential damage to other building elements. You should describe any evidence of previous structural repairs which have been undertaken.

There is no general requirement to give an indication of the underlying causes of the defect, or to give an impression of the extent of remedial work required to put the defect right. Similarly, there is no requirement to give an indication of the recommended treatment, or the cost of any such treatment. In considering the appropriate condition rating, you will need to take account of any cost of works and make a note of likely costs in your site notes, but will not be required to show your workings in the HCR.

In the case of structural movement, which would be reported in Section C of the Home Condition Report, you should follow the usual rules of describing any problems, and provide an opinion as to whether you consider the movement is serious or ongoing, and if so to recommend further investigation.

In the case of dampness (Section E9), you should express a view on whether any dampness identified should be classified as 'penetrating dampness, rising dampness or condensation'. You should also express a view as to the likely cause of the dampness and, if appropriate, give a warning that the dampness may affect other parts of the property.

Occasionally, dampness and timber problems can be very pervasive within a building, and may well appear in several building elements, possibly having spread from others. In such cases, you should mention all elements in which the defect appears. If it is not possible to determine the source of the defect, choose the element which is likely to be the most seriously damaged as the primary element. In addition, consider describing such defects against the heading '*Widespread Problems that Affect Many Parts of the Property*', under '*Summary of Ratings*' in Section B of the HCR.

The treatment of Sections D, E, F and G assume a high degree of organisation on the part of the Home Inspector, particularly if the HCR is to be usable and acceptable to the consumer. However, this does not necessarily conform with the way that information is gathered during an inspection, when the defects and problems of a building are gradually revealed and understood. It is therefore important that the site records taken as part of the data collection process are not simply transcribed into the HCR form, but are digested and rearranged into a complete and coherent report.

In some cases it will be possible to predict, with a reasonable degree of accuracy the likely performance of individual building elements, in particular as a consequence of their age or nature of design or construction. They will possess certain performance characteristics, based upon typical repairs or defects known to affect them.

Figure 3.3 clarifies the decision process when considering the categorisation of a building element's condition against urgency, seriousness and cost criteria.

WHEN A DEFECT IS NOT A DEFECT

The Home Condition Report is essentially concerned with applying a condition rating against individual building elements, but there could be situations where it is difficult to decide how to report upon certain defects. This is particularly important when considering older listed or historic buildings as their performance characteristics differ.

For a **defect** to exist there must be evidence of at least one of the following:

- physical damage;
- instability;
- wear and tear;
- impaired function;
- impaired serviceability;
- inadequacy in original construction;
- inadequacy of previous repair works;
- threat to the health, safety or security of the occupants;
- threat to the general comfort of the occupants; and
- a situation constituting a continuing threat to the fabric of the property.

An example condition rating exercise is included in Appendix C.

'URGENT, IMMEDIATE AND SERIOUS DEFECTS'

When determining defects, **urgent** or **immediate** refers to the type of work that needs to be carried out within a matter of a few weeks or months, and certainly within six months of the inspection.

An **urgent** defect is likely to:

- rapidly develop into a serious defect if not repaired/remedied immediately; or

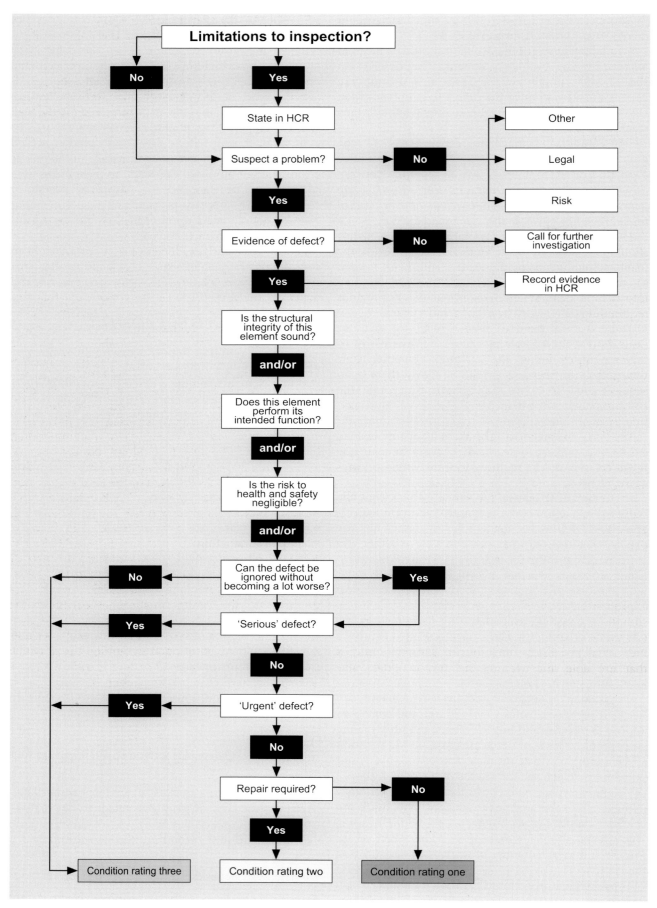

Figure 3.3: The HCR decision path

- cause structural failure or serious defects in other building elements if not repaired/remedied immediately.

A **serious** defect is likely to:

- have a high cost associated with it;
- compromise the structural integrity of the property;
- compromise the intended function of the building element; or
- affect the health and safety of the occupants.

In making a judgment about urgency, no consideration should be given to the cost of likely remedial works – a job can be urgent without being costly! In considering the *seriousness* of a defect, you should take account of the need for any required works that have significant cost associated with them. Clearly, as the HCR does not set out to provide cost information, or a valuation, the Home Inspector is not required to show any workings in the report, but may need to provide adequate evidence of their justification in the notes taken on site. Therefore, an indicative broad budget figure is all that is required for this purpose. It should reflect the likely cost charged for a repair (or series of repairs) by a professional tradesman complying with the relevant health and safety precautions.

The cost assessment should be taken as the expenditure required to deal with all the defects included within the relevant building elements where category two or category three building elements have been identified. If a defect has consequences for other building elements, the cost should be taken as that associated with all the works required to deal with the defect and all its consequences.

Reference to the **BCIS Guide to House Rebuilding Costs** is recommended as a source of published information in this area and is suitable for checking appropriate levels of cost in a variety of different situations. In addition, **BCIS Rebuild Online** (www.bcis.co.uk) calculates rebuilding costs for individual properties, including adjustment options that are able, for example, to produce date and location-specific results.

REFERRALS TO SPECIALISTS AND RECOMMENDING FURTHER ADVICE

Home Inspectors will be expected to make definite decisions and judgments when completing the Home Condition Report, and generally there should be very few occasions on which recommending further advice will be required.

On occasions, the extent of inspection may be insufficient for the Home Inspector to form an opinion or to report adequately on some aspect of a building element where a defect is suspected. There may be a need for further opening-up of the structure, testing of components or other exploratory work. In some cases, a definitive judgment on a defect may require skills in which the Home Inspector is lacking. In such circumstances, the Home Inspector can recommend the need for further advice. It is important that this option should not be used as a defensive 'buck-passing' strategy on the part of the Home Inspector. Recommending further advice should only be included when there is a specific justifiable concern that cannot be tackled by the Home Inspector. In any event, the justification for such a recommendation should be outlined against the primary element (with which the suspected defect is associated) in the HCR.

In the majority of cases where recommending further advice, the defect would fall into the 'serious' or 'urgent' category and a category three condition rating will need to be assigned by the Home Inspector.

The precise wording to be used by Home Inspectors when recommending the need for further advice will be laid down in the text entries which will form the mandatory and standard phrasing for the HCR. The standard phrasing used in this context throughout Sections D, E and F is expressed as '*Further advice should be obtained*' and deliberately avoids any mention of 'specialist investigation' because the report may be relied upon by a variety of people, and each will have their own needs. Stating the need for further advice should be mentioned in Sections D, E and F alongside the primary element, and it should also be reported in summary form in Section B.

4 Producing Home Condition Reports

What they say about surveyors is probably true… '*get ten of them in a room to look at the same defect and they will come up with ten different answers.*' Such a situation is wholly unacceptable to consumers in the Home Information Pack environment.

OBJECTIVITY VERSUS SUBJECTIVITY

Perhaps the most noticeable change in emphasis introduced by the HCR is the requirement for Home Inspectors to write a report that objectively describes the condition of the property. This requires Home Inspectors to bring an unbiased and fair approach to the whole exercise and to consider all relevant evidence to ensure that the condition of the property is fairly represented. People's homes are a potentially very controversial subject, so the Home Inspector must be very wary of making statements without using supporting evidence. The stronger and more complete the evidence, the better.

Evidence is strong when:

- you have found a number of consistent indicators;
- your evidence can be verified, if necessary through opening-up, monitoring or testing;
- other Home Inspectors would have come to the same conclusion;
- you report hard facts rather than pure opinions; and
- your findings are consistent with the established professional body of knowledge.

Home Inspectors need to constantly put themselves into the shoes of the person reading the report in order to make certain that all the information provided in the report is relevant and not trying to 'blind them with science'. One of the main challenges will be the need to produce readable reports that are written in objective language, describing the defects in sufficient depth to enable them to be understood, without the need to comment on whether or not these defects are likely to affect the marketability of the property. Gaining an acceptable level of consistency between Home Inspectors in general will also be crucial for the smooth running of the scheme.

As consistent reporting will be a fundamental requirement of the HCR, the Home Inspector Certification Board (HICB) is to introduce a core of 'standard text' that may be used by Home Inspectors on a day-to-day basis. This will include lender's 'mandatory' paragraphs in respect of Sections B and C of the HCR. The use of standard or 'preferred' text elsewhere within the report will be encouraged where it is appropriate, but clearly some flexibility in approach is required, including freestyle personalisation of reporting to cater for the wide range of housing types and defects typically seen in the UK.

DRAFTING, WRITING AND REVISING THE REPORT

It is almost impossible to define precisely what a good writing style is. In the context of the HCR, the ability to get your message across each time you produce a Home Condition Report is probably the nearest working definition.

Drafting

Taking time to collect and handle all the information from the inspection along with preparing, planning and possibly revising your report will give you a practical blueprint for a successful HCR. This further emphasises the need for comprehensive notes to be made at the time of inspection so that the evidence recorded can be assembled into a true and accurate HCR. Incorporating information collected from desk-based research and pre-inspection questions asked of the owner or agent will also be a relevant consideration at this point.

Before writing the report, it is suggested that you make a sufficient record of the property to provide an initial overview before beginning to draft the report. This may not always be possible if you collect data and produce your HCR by means of a handheld personal computer or similar device, but typically this type of system (if written properly), will allow you to review and revise the report after the event, so the effect is the same.

Writing

Sections B and C of the HCR require the Home Inspector's findings to be incorporated into an introduction to, and an overall considered view of the property. These HCR entries are concerned with the whole of the property, and are intended to summarise its condition while providing a synopsis of associated risks. The summary must follow logically from the Home Inspector's detailed findings. It should include as much relevant information as the intended readers need to know before they read the rest of the report.

The summary is all important and requires particular attention to ensure that views are expressed accurately and unambiguously, while reflecting findings contained elsewhere in the main body of the HCR. It must represent a true summary of the HCR itself and should highlight any particular aspects related to the property that require particular emphasis. The summary is intended to provide a digest of what the consumer is about to read, should stimulate their attention and focus upon salient facts.

To be successful, the HCR you produce must ensure that the buyer, the seller and the lender will be able to:

- read it with ease;
- understand everything in it without undue effort;
- accept the facts, findings and summary; and
- understand what (if any) further advice or investigations should be obtained.

Achieving these objectives demands that Home Inspectors convey their message effectively and communicate in a way that is consistent, clear and intelligible to the audience. Every situation in which a report is prepared will vary and the way each point is expressed needs to be drafted with care. HCR reporting requires a style where sentences and paragraphs are constructed in a way that enables information to be conveyed both speedily and accurately to the reader. This is often very difficult to achieve, but has to be the main objective for any Home Inspector, particularly as once the report has been issued, there will be no opportunity to explain or expand upon your findings, or modify what you have written.

There will be no opportunity to reinforce your message and the readers cannot get further assistance from you other than on 'points of clarification'. Readers have to work on their own to understand what the Home Inspector has said and to quantify the meanings. If the report is written in a bad style, the reader may get the wrong meaning, or perhaps no meaning at all. The constant aim of the Home Inspector should be to make the readers' task easier. Using a reporting style which is clear, concise and direct, using short sentences, with familiar words and without jargon expressions, will therefore be important in achieving these aims.

Revising

Checking and amending the report is a time consuming, but fundamental part of the process of producing a successful HCR. The pressure to finish a report as quickly as possible will be a factor to consider, but once you have completed your first draft, you need to read it for the first time. At this stage you should ask yourself:

- Does the report flow?
- Have you conveyed the meaning you had intended?
- Is the technical content expressed in plain language?
- Are there adequate signposts for the intended readers?
- Can you justify everything that you have written?
- Is the information as factually correct as possible?
- Is the information as accurate and as complete as possible?
- Are there any obvious factual errors, ambiguities, omissions or other mistakes?
- Is there any irrelevant information that should be removed?
- Is the HCR well presented? For example, are there any word processing errors, spelling mistakes, inconsistencies in font sizes and styles, is the page and item numbering correct, are the margins and spacing correct?

Redrafting the report will enable you to reflect and respond to each of these points in turn, so that after the proposed final draft is produced, you should be able to ask yourself:

- Have you used the appropriate standard text responses where required to do so?
- Is the HCR compliant with the *Home Inspector Inspection and Reporting Requirements*?
- Is the HCR compliant with the Duties and Responsibilities of the Home Inspector?

THE ROLE OF HCR REGISTRATION ORGANISATIONS

Home Inspectors will be required to deliver an electronic copy of the Home Condition Report under quality controlled conditions, via one of the commercial HCR Registration organisations. Once the report is lodged by the HCR Registration organisation, it becomes a matter of public record, although those with user access and PIN numbers will be entitled to view the information. Long-term storage of HCRs will be provided by means of a single central electronic archive.

The key purpose of these electronic data-banking organisations is to ensure that the data delivered to them is safely stored and managed, readily available to all those entitled to access it and in particular, that the transfer of data to lenders and others is as secure as required. It will also enable easy ongoing monitoring of standards to ensure that the quality of HCRs is at an acceptable level. It also provides a degree of transparency for consumers, as well as introduces important checks and balances to reduce risks of data tampering.

In order to be able to create and store an authorised HCR under the new arrangements, it will be important to link-up with one or more of the commercial HCR Registration organisations.

Figure 4.1 illustrates the flow of information from the beginning of the marketing process through to the granting of a mortgage.

HOW THE PRODUCTION PROCESS DIFFERS FROM PRESENT ARRANGEMENTS

As a result of recent developments in information technology, there are a number of companies offering a standardised approach to on-site data capture, and automatic report writing facilities are already available to deliver reports to clients electronically through the internet.

For a number of years, facilities have been available that enable surveyors to dictate reports to a central typing resource by telephone. Further research and development is underway to provide Home Inspectors with a variety of means to produce their reports more speedily and in a more risk-controlled way. Future

solutions are likely to include production of reports using voice or command activated 'report generators', utilising either a PDA, palmtop, tablet or laptop computer either on site or from the car or office after the inspection. Undoubtedly, by the time that HCRs become mandatory, information and communication technology will have advanced even further, helping to produce HCRs that are more consistent between Home Inspectors, and simpler to understand for consumers.

Production of the final HCR will be entirely electronic, via the internet, and so it will be essential for Home Inspectors to use broadband internet access, a web browser and simple email facility.

Home Inspectors should expect to receive instructions from a variety of different sources, including:

- large HIP providers;
- estate agents;
- mortgage lenders;
- panel managers; and
- members of the general public.

Before the inspection is carried out, the Home Inspector, estate agent or HIP provider will request an authorisation from a HCR Registration organisation, which will come in the form of a unique code and URRN (Unique Report Reference Number).

The Home Inspector will send the completed HCR to the HCR Registration organisation via the internet, and an encrypted electronic message will then be sent back to acknowledge its arrival. At that stage, the Home

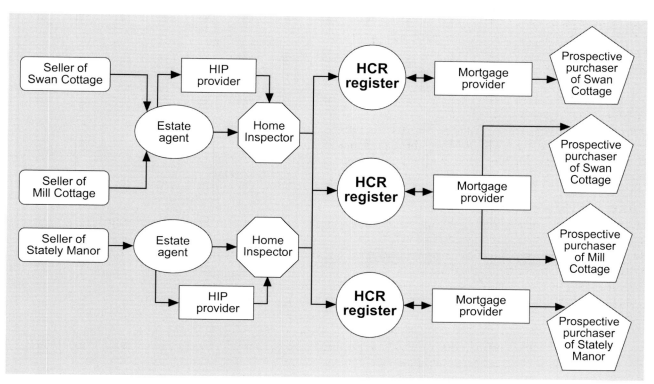

Figure 4.1: Information roadmap for a HCR

Inspector is able to provide the client with a copy of the HCR in whatever format and through whichever delivery method had been agreed previously, e.g. faxing or posting a paper copy, or emailing an electronic version. Figure 4.2 illustrates the various procedures surrounding a HCR's production, including exchange of information, verification and data storage, as well as post production procedures such as billing and complaints handling.

After a report is produced and uploaded by the HCR Registration organisation to the central archive, it becomes a matter of public record. The HCR cannot be altered in any way after this stage. If there is a serious mistake in the report, and of course this will be a matter of fact and degree, a facility will be available for the named client or the Home Inspector to apply to the Certification Scheme to have the report removed from the record and replaced.

The HCR will not have a finite shelf life, because it is intended to represent a snapshot of a property's record of condition on the day of inspection. A report may be produced and then not used for e.g. six months, but it is still valid as a record of condition and does not become out of date purely as a result of time passing. In theory, circumstances could affect the property during such a time period, such as damage to a chimney stack after a storm. However, once the report is posted on the databank, the principle of public record means that the HCR can remain in use. Undoubtedly, when changes take place to a property

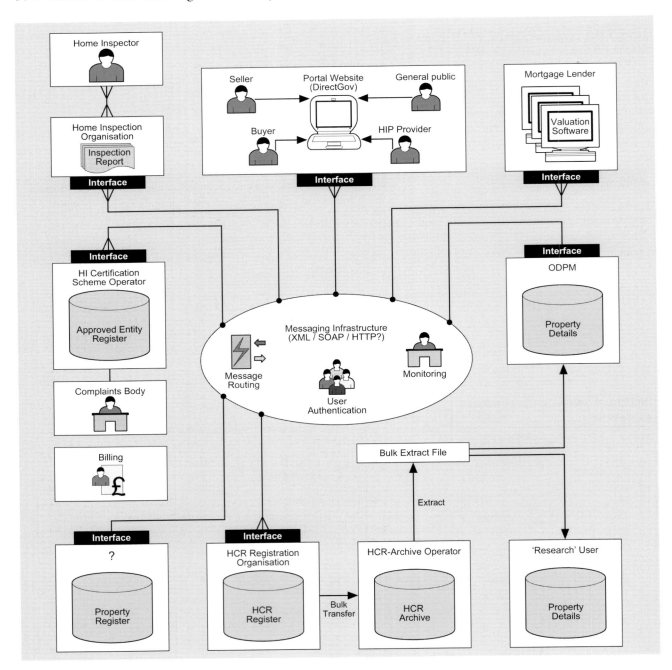

Figure 4.2: HCR procedures

after a HCR has been produced, such as repairs or alterations, it is in the seller's best interests to show this information in some way. The seller (or agent) will be able to include the quotation and receipted invoice for any works in the HIP, so that prospective buyers have a complete picture of the property's condition. As a more expensive alternative, the buyer may want to commission a second HCR. In this event, there would be two reports logged on the databank and the prospective buyer is entitled to see both.

HSV/HCR COMPARISON BETWEEN METHODS OF REPORTING

For the Home Condition Report to be seen as completely fair, impartial and authoritative, an entirely new and more disciplined approach to report writing is required. Many of the report elements that need to be avoided in the HCR are commonplace in the HSV. Table 4.1 highlights some of the issues to be avoided and included when dictating a Home Condition Report.

Table 4.1: Methods of reporting: What to avoid and include in a HCR

What to avoid/include in a HCR

AVOID: Irrelevant or inconclusive facts and conjecture **INCLUDE:** Relevant and conclusive facts based on evidence that is capable of being proved	Speculating that dry rot may exist behind plasterboard dry-lined panelling without any supporting evidence, such as dampness, rippling of the finishes or lack of ventilation will be regarded as too conjectural.
AVOID: Subjective comments, opinion and bias **INCLUDE:** Objective, authoritative information and comments	Reporting that the kitchen units are in a 'filthy state', or decorations are 'tasteless' or 'old-fashioned' will be too subjective for the HCR, and likely to cause offence.
AVOID: Precautionary comments and unnecessary caveats **INCLUDE:** Balanced, fair assessment	Standard caveats covering the possible risk of future failure are commonplace in survey reports. One example is the potential for deterioration and misting of double-glazed sealed unit window panes. For the HCR, simply describing the current condition of the element is generally what is required.
AVOID: Speculative comments **INCLUDE:** Specific comments	Speculative comments regarding the condition of unseen cavity wall ties without any supporting evidence (such as horizontal splitting of mortar jointing or 'pagoda effect' of gable walls), will be regarded as too speculative.
AVOID: Future planned and preventive maintenance issues **INCLUDE:** Reference to present condition in a clear and direct style	There will be situations where an element would benefit from attention by way of routine maintenance, such as a slightly moss covered roof. This can be addressed in the HCR by applying the appropriate condition rating, but more extensive planned or preventive maintenance is generally not reported in the HCR.
AVOID: Reference to the buildings' shortcomings or deficiencies, unless the mandatory text requires you to do so **INCLUDE:** Reference to condition and defects	Unless built recently, the property is likely to have a number of shortcomings, particularly if compared with up-to-date Building Regulations. Generally, such deficiencies are not reported and can be addressed in the HCR by applying the appropriate condition rating to the element. However, if they are specific 'ring-fenced' health and safety risks, they need to be reported accordingly in Section C of the HCR.
AVOID: Repair solutions **INCLUDE:** No reference to repair solutions or associated costs	Old style survey reports required the surveyor to provide an opinion regarding how to repair the element, such as 'The chimney stack requires raking and repointing with sand/lime mortar.' Due to the need for objectivity in the HCR, repair solutions are not required.
AVOID: Detailed technical descriptions **INCLUDE:** Non-technical subject matter	Describing an element in an overly technical way, such as through the use of complicated formulae/measurements or technical jargon will only serve to obscure the meaning of the report.
AVOID: Jargon **INCLUDE:** Plain language, short words and sentences	Language that is specific to surveying and the use of terminology and words such as 'bungaroosh' and 'clunch' may mean something to the professional producing the report, but very little to the lay reader. Such jargon should be explained to aid the reader's understanding. For example, reference to 'flashings' would be better referred to as 'the weatherproofing between the roof and the chimney stack'.
AVOID: Consideration of value **INCLUDE:** Consideration of condition and not value	Valuations are not required for the HCR.
AVOID: General health and safety advice **INCLUDE:** Comments on 'ring-fenced' health and safety issues specifically listed in Section C	Only specific comments relating to the list of 'ring-fenced' health and safety issues need to be mentioned, in Section C of the HCR. Potential risks that do not generally need to be reported include trip hazards or a slippery oil spillage on an external pathway.

5 Case study: HSV and HCR property reports

This chapter contains a real life case study property, presented by a series of photographs along with a completed Homebuyer Survey and Valuation (HSV) and Home Condition Report (HCR). The house contains some obvious defects and deficiencies, and closer views are provided to show its form and construction. **The purpose of this case study is to provide a comparison of the two report formats, showing clear distinctions between their content, emphasis and overall reporting styles.**

OVERVIEW

The case study property is a Victorian mid-terraced house built around 1880. It is typical of its type and located in an older suburb of Piketown-on-Sea. For the purpose of the HSV, we have assumed that the house has been purchased by your client on the open market at £150,000.

The HCR inspection of this house took approximately 110 minutes – around the same amount of time needed to carry out an equivalent HSV inspection. Additional data needed to be collected to enable the RdSAP calculation to be undertaken, which required some additional measuring of (e.g. floor to ceiling heights), as well as taking more detailed information for the central heating boiler.

Front elevation taken from the main road

Lower front elevation

Upper front elevation

Upper rear elevation

Lower rear elevation

View of upper rear addition elevation

View of reveal around first floor rear window opening

View of rear chimney breast from within roof space

The following pages include the property's two contrasting reports. Please note that in order to display the full scope of the HCR format, but to save unnecessary repetition, the HCR for this property contains various parts that are not included in the additional reports that appear later in the book. This includes generic or static pages such as those outlining '*The role of the home inspector and the home condition report*', and notes regarding '*When the report is complete*'. In addition, data entry fields that are not relevant to the property concerned (such as the various entry fields relating to flats and maisonettes)

have been left in this property's HCR to help illustrate the full scope of the report form. Where the HCR for this property contains data entry fields that would be omitted under normal reporting circumstances, these have been highlighted accordingly.

The energy performance certificates in the case study HCR, along with the further energy performance certificates in the next chapter's HCRs, have been generated by Elmhurst Energy Systems. The energy performance certificate is still undergoing development and its final format will be subject to change.

THE RICS
HOMEBUYER
SURVEY & VALUATION

The Property: 121 Victorian Villas
                       Piketown-on-Sea
                       Pikeshire MM1 1MN

The Clients: Mr and Mrs Fish

Inspected on: 2nd December 2005

Inspected by: JR Hartley
                       Home Inspectors.co.uk Ltd
                       1 High Street
                       Tenchtown
                       Pikeshire MM1 2SS

 RICS
BOOKS

HOMEBUYER THE SURVEY 1

THE RICS
SURVEY & VALUATION

A: INTRODUCTION

**PLEASE READ
THIS PAGE WITH
EXTRA CARE**

- OBJECTIVE
- CONTENT
- ACTION
- OVERALL
  OPINION

Please note that this Report is solely for your use and your professional advisers', and no liability to anyone else is accepted. Should you not act upon advice contained in the Report, no responsibility is accepted for the consequences. [Standard Terms of Engagement, Clause 6]

The Report has been prepared in line with the *Description of the HOMEBUYER Service* already provided (an additional copy is attached). If any addition to the standard Service was agreed before the Inspection, this is confirmed at the foot of the last page.

Objective

The principal objective of the Report and Valuation is to assist you to:

- make a reasoned and informed judgement on whether or not to proceed with the purchase;
- assess at what price it would be reasonable to purchase the Property;
- be clear what decisions and actions should be taken:
  - in ENGLAND AND WALES before contracts are exchanged;
  - in SCOTLAND before concluding an offer to purchase.

Content

The general condition and particular features of the Property are covered, but the Report focuses on the matters which I judge to be urgent or significant.

Urgent matters are defects judged to be an actual or developing threat to the fabric of the building; it will be advisable to have these put right as soon as possible after purchase (in some cases even before). *Significant matters* are defined as matters which could reasonably be expected in negotiations over price to be reflected in the amount finally agreed.

Matters assessed as *not urgent* or *not significant* are outside the scope of the HOMEBUYER Service, and are generally not reported. However, other matters (such as legal and safety considerations) may be reported where I judge this to be helpful and constructive.

ACTION

If – after reading and considering all the information and advice in the Report – you decide to proceed with the purchase, then there are probably some things on which you should take action at once. Each such item is highlighted in the Report with the word ACTION and is also listed in Section F: *Summary* together with advice on what to do next.

OVERALL OPINION

Below are my conclusions, in brief, on the price at which it would be reasonable to purchase the Property, and on particular features which affect its present value and may affect its future resale. The opinion takes no account of factors outside the scope of the HOMEBUYER Service.

It is hoped that this overall view will help you to keep in perspective the detailed facts and advice which follow. You are asked to bear in mind particularly that it can be misleading to treat individual matters in isolation. So that you may use this Report to best advantage in reaching your decision on whether or not to proceed with the purchase of this Property, *you are most strongly advised to read and consider its contents as a whole.*

The property is considered to be a reasonable proposition for purchase at the agreed purchase price, which is understood to be £150,000. This opinion is based on the presumption that you are prepared to accept the cost and inconvenience of dealing with the various repair/improvement works reported. Provided that the necessary works are carried out to a satisfactory standard, there should not be any particular difficulties on resale in normal market conditions.

Subjective opinion about the reasonableness of the agreed purchase price is no longer required. The HCR requires Home Inspectors to avoid any reference to value, agreed price, or future saleability.

HOMEBUYER THE SURVEY 2

B: THE PROPERTY & LOCATION

This section covers the important general background information on the Property and its location, including amenities and features of the vicinity as well as any environmental and other wider considerations. It also includes who appeared to be in occupation, the weather at the time of the Inspection, and any limitations on the Inspection.

> *Please note* that, throughout the Report, the principal features and parts of a property are given in the left-hand margin thus: – often followed by a list of supplementary items, such as:
>
> **B I**
> **THE PROPERTY**
> ■ Type and age

B I
THE PROPERTY
■ Type and age
■ Construction
■ Accommodation
■ Garage and grounds

B2
THE LOCATION

B3
**CIRCUMSTANCES OF
THE INSPECTION**

*Categorising
the property
in this way is
not required
for the HCR.*

B1: THE PROPERTY

Type and Age: The property comprises a mid-terraced house built around the end of the Victorian period (probably around 1880), which was constructed at that time with a two storey rear addition. In addition to this, there is a single storey rear extension which was probably added during the 1950s and now forms the cloakroom and rear entrance lobby.

Construction: The property is conventionally built in a traditional style for its age. The roof surfaces are clad with interlocking concrete tiles and the walls are of solid brick, parts of which are of single skin construction. The ground floors are partly of solid concrete construction and partly of timber boarding on joist construction. The first floors are boarded on timber joists.

*Information
about
orientation
will not be
required for
the HCR.*

The front of the property faces roughly south-east.

Accommodation: The accommodation comprises:
Ground Floor:
Entrance Hall
Living Room
Dining Room
Kitchen
Small Rear Lobby
Cloakroom/WC

First Floor:
Front Bedroom
Rear Bedroom with connecting door to Bathroom/WC

*The topography of the
site and its location
are all issues to be
avoided in the HCR,
along with any
similar factors that
could influence
saleability.*

Garage and Grounds: There is no front garden and no garage. There is a small rear garden.

B2: LOCATION
The property occupies a site which slopes gently downwards from rear to front within a high density, mainly residential area close to the centre of Piketown-on-Sea. There are scattered commercial uses within the neighbourhood and the property overlooks a primary school, (factors which could deter some future purchasers).

B3: CIRCUMSTANCES OF THE INSPECTION
The inspection that we have carried out is of the visible elements of construction of the property only. In conducting our survey and completing our report, we have had to make certain assumptions and restrictions as to the scope and application of the report. These are set out in our standard Terms and Conditions, included within this report.

*Third person 'we'
and 'our' becomes
passive or first
person 'I' and 'my'.*

The property was vacant and unfurnished, although the majority of floors were covered with fitted carpets which prevented a full inspection.

The weather was dry at the time of inspection.

*Repeating
caveats in
this way will
not be
necessary in
the HCR.*

HOMEBUYER THE SURVEY 3

THE RICS
SURVEY & VALUATION

C: THE BUILDING

**PLEASE READ
THESE NOTES**

Movement, timber defects and dampness are, in their various forms, the three greatest potential threats to the structure of a building. Where evidence is found of any of these conditions, advice is given on what action should be taken. (Where a problem is judged to be serious, it might prove necessary for a separate, detailed examination to be undertaken – perhaps by specialists. For example, the foundations might have to be laid open to analyse the cause of some structural movement, or the full extent of timber defects might require further investigation.)

**C1
MOVEMENT**

C1: MOVEMENT

The building shows signs of some past structural movement. For example, hairline cracking, chiefly around window and door openings, together with minor distortion and unevenness and slight cambering of some window sills. The heaviest cracking was noted beneath the bathroom window on the rear gable wall. In addition to this, gaps have developed between the walls and the adjacent window/door frames.

**C2
TIMBER DEFECTS**

We found no evidence of recent or progressive movement affecting the main structure of the building, and consider that the likelihood of any further significant movement is remote. The movement is typical of a property of this age and type.

**C3
DAMPNESS**

C2: TIMBER DEFECTS

**C4
CONDENSATION
& INSULATION**

We made random inspections of exposed and accessible timbers and found evidence of woodworm infestation and wet rot within the old timbers. For example, within the stairs, the living room underfloor area, the ground floor timbers generally and to a lesser extent, the loft timbers.

We noted evidence of previous wet rot decay to the joist ends visible from within the cellar and these have now been cut back and renewed satisfactorily.

In view of the high ground levels, the general limited underfloor ventilation and instances of dampness, there is potential for timber decay in adjacent timber work.

So far as we can judge, the wood beetle infestation is largely inactive although some areas particularly within the understair cupboard appear relatively fresh.

It will therefore be necessary for you to have the building inspected, including relevant underfloor areas, by a specialist timber treatment contractor and to carry out any essential works under long term insurance backed guarantee.

ACTION: You are advised to obtain a specialist's report together with quotations for treatment. Please also see Section F1.

C3: DAMPNESS

Damp Proof Course: Although the building has been provided with a partial chemical injection damp proof course, evidence of rising damp was found (see below).

The remedial damp proofing works may well have been carried out under guarantee. This may cover at least part of the cost of repair, so it is important that your legal adviser take up this enquiry as soon as possible. Please also see Section E3.

Rising and Penetrating Damp: Random tests for dampness were carried out using a moisture meter.

At ground floor level we noted traces of dampness around skirting level within the front left hand corner of the living room, the rear wall of the dining room and the left hand and rear wall to the kitchen. The dampness appears to be rising through the bases of these walls in the areas tested.

Rising damp often leaves salts in the inside wall plaster. As well as eliminating the rising damp, plaster may need to be replaced, often requiring other works such as renewing skirting boards.
ACTION: In case the damp proofing guarantee will not cover the cost, you are advised to obtain a specialist's report, together with quotations for necessary work. Please see Section F1.

Condensation: No indications of any problems with condensation were noted. However, condensation may be a problem for one occupier where it was not for the previous one. It can often be controlled by careful management of heating and ventilation.

C4: INSULATION

Insulation in the loft is below the standard now recommended. Upgrading may be worthwhile.

The slender external walls to the back addition will allow considerable heat loss. You may wish to consider introducing an insulated lining internally.

© THE ROYAL INSTITUTION
OF CHARTERED SURVEYORS
2005

Structural movement will be an issue of importance to buyers, sellers and lenders, and is therefore included in Section B of the HCR.

Within the HCR, timber defects such as woodworm or rot will be dealt with against each individual element, but may need to be drawn together as a widespread problem affecting many parts of the property (Section B of the HCR).

ACTION points of this type are not required for the HCR.

In the HCR, there is no need to state the obvious or repeat what has been stated in the Terms of Engagement.

This would be a matter for conveyancers to include in their enquiries and would be reported accordingly under Section C of the HCR.

Where further investigation is required, this will be reported in a very prescribed manner in Section B of the HCR.

Any comments regarding dampness, including 'damp proof course' are to be included in Sections D4 and E9 of the HCR.

Speculative comments such as these are to be avoided in the HCR.

ACTION items will not be required in the HCR.

Any reference to thermal efficiency, levels of insulation and suggested improvements will be addressed in Section H of the HCR.

Reference in this way to (future) occupation will be excluded from the HCR.

In the HCR, this would need to be reported under the relevant building element (Section E3).

THE SURVEY 4

Roof structure will be reported as an individual building element, in Section E1 of the HCR.

Comments such as these are too subjective for the HCR.

Subjective words are to be avoided in favour of the HCR's focus towards factual description.

C: THE BUILDING (continued)

The roofs, chimneys and other external surfaces of the building are examined from ground level, where necessary from adjoining public property and with the help of binoculars. The roof structure is examined from inside the roof space where accessible (insulation material, stored goods and other contents are not moved or lifted). The efficiency of rainwater fittings (gutters and downpipes) can only be assessed properly during the Inspection if there is heavy rain.

PLEASE READ THESE NOTES

Deficiencies and predictions relating to future maintenance are generally omitted from the HCR, but may be reflected in the condition rating.

C5
THE EXTERIOR
- Roof structure and covering
- Chimneys
- Rainwater fittings
- Main walls
- External joinery and decoration
- Other

C5: THE EXTERIOR
Roof Structure and Covering: There is no obvious evidence to indicate significant weakness in the timbers making up the roof structure.

The roof coverings are generally in a satisfactory condition where visible. A small number of individual tiles have slightly lifted, but this is not affecting the weather tightness of the roof covering. The majority of individual tiles where these could be viewed with the aid of binoculars were found to be in a reasonable condition for their age.

Too subjective for the HCR.

At present, the brick parapets alongside the roof do not make adequate provision for damp proofing and have no copings or drip mouldings. As a consequence, there is an increased risk of damp penetration.

Chimneys: The two brick built chimneys are generally in satisfactory condition.

Opinion regarding deficiency, therefore not included in the HCR.

Some cracking has developed to the top sections of the rear chimney stack. It is likely that the flaunchings around the top of this stack has also deteriorated to some extent. Although no evidence of damp penetration was identified, the cracked mortar jointing and flaunchings are likely to need repointing in due course.

Future maintenance prediction, therefore not included in the HCR.

The brickwork to both chimney stacks has become distorted, particularly to the top sections of brickwork, due to the action of chemicals over the years.

Rainwater Fittings: These are in a generally fair condition, but the gutter to the back addition has become damaged and will need to be replaced.

Caveats such as these are to be avoided in the HCR.

The down pipe discharge arrangements are poor and ideally should be improved.

Future maintenance prediction, therefore not included in the HCR.

In a number of places the gutters and gullies are blocked with moss, silt and other debris, most notably to the rear addition where rainwater overspillage has begun to occur. The fittings need an overhaul, including cleaning and checking for alignment.

ACTION: You are advised to obtain quotations for the necessary work. Please also see Section F1.

Repair solutions are outside the scope of the HCR.

Main Walls: In the absence of instructions to fully expose the foundations of the external and internal walls, you must accept the risks of unseen defects. The wall surfaces as seen within the limitations of inspection are generally in a satisfactory condition and no significant defects were noted.

ACTION items are not required in the HCR.

It will be necessary to point-up the gaps which have developed around the window and door openings, as there may be a risk of damp penetration.

The two stone window sills at the front of the building at first floor level have become badly spalled due to frost and damp deterioration, and require repair. In their present damaged state, the sills are more at risk of dampness entering the building below the window sills, although no evidence of this was identified.

This would represent a hazard and would need to be reported accordingly in Section C of the HCR.

ACTION: You are advised to obtain quotations for the necessary work. Please also see Section F1.

Precautionary comments of this type are to be excluded from the HCR.

External Joinery: The external doors are of timber, partly glazed. Repairs are required to the front door, which is swollen and the rear door, which is ill-fitting. The light weight glazing should be replaced using toughened or safety glass, as this could represent a hazard.

The original windows are of painted timber sashes. The front bedroom and bathroom windows have been replaced with very poor quality louvre windows, whilst those to the cellar and cloakroom are timber casement. Their general condition is poor; some of the windows are affected by wet rot and overhauling, repairs and renewals should be anticipated.

Very subjective comments are to be excluded from the HCR.

Speculative warnings regarding possible future repairs are to be excluded from the HCR.

ACTION: You are advised to obtain quotations for the necessary work. Please also see Section F1.

External Decoration: The decorations are in a poor overall condition. A good deal of blistering, peeling and general wear and tear deterioration has occurred. Redecoration is required to external timberwork generally.

ACTION: You are advised to obtain quotations for the necessary work. Please also see Section F1.

Other: None.

ACTION items are not required in the HCR.

Speculative repair solution, therefore not to be included in the HCR.

In the HCR, subjective reporting will be replaced with factual and objective reporting.

THE RICS HOMEBUYER SURVEY & VALUATION

THE SURVEY

5

PLEASE READ THESE NOTES

C6 THE INTERIOR
- Roof space
- Ceilings
- Floors
- Internal walls and partitions
- Fireplaces, etc.
- Internal joinery and decoration
- Other

C: THE BUILDING *(continued)*

Floor surfaces and under-floor spaces are examined so far as they are accessible (furniture, floor coverings and other contents are not moved or lifted). If a part or area normally examined was found to be not accessible, this is reported; if a problem is suspected, advice is given on what action should be taken. It is not possible to assess the internal condition of any chimney, boiler or other flues. (In some cases, furnishings may conceal defects.)

C6: THE INTERIOR

Roof Space: Access to the main and rear addition roof space was obtained by means of a cupboard just off the front bedroom.

No evidence of significant defect was found.

The roof slopes are under felted. The under felting precluded an inspection of the battens and tiles. There was no physical access into the ground floor back addition roof space.

Ceilings: Ceilings comprise a mixture of the original, dated lath and plaster, with some replacement plasterboard. There is also a hard boarded ceiling over the stairwell. These are in a generally satisfactory condition.

Some minor cracking was noted in places and some bulging of the ceiling in the kitchen. Repairs to ceilings should be anticipated in the long term.

Floors: The floors to the hall and main ground floor reception rooms are of timber boarding with cellar and air space below. The kitchen, rear entrance lobby and cloakroom floors are of solid construction. The cellar has a solid floor with linoleum covering. The first floor is of timber boarding on joists.

Ideally, ventilation should be improved to sub-floor areas at ground floor level.

ACTION: You are advised to obtain quotations for the necessary work. Please also see Section F1.

Slight deflection and springiness was noted to the timber floors as is to be expected in a property of this age and type. The majority of the timber joist ends as seen from within the cellar have been renewed in recent years following a previous rot problem (please see further comments under timber decay).

Internal Walls and Partitions: The walls are formed in a mixture of solid and timber stud construction, most of which is lath and plaster or plasterboard faced.

General hairline cracking was noted. The cracking is due to shrinkage/expansion and minor settlement within the structure, and is not of serious structural significance.

The plastered surfaces are generally uneven and some damage was noted in places.

Some of the walls in this property have been dry lined. Whilst there are no signs of significant defect, it must be appreciated that in an old building there is a risk of decay in timbers fixed to solid walls which are affected by damp.

Fireplaces: The chimney breasts within the rear bedroom and dining room have been removed and are supported upon metal brackets within the main roof space. No evidence of significant crack damage or distress was found around these alterations.

It is important that any fireplaces that are to remain out of use should be capped externally and ventilated internally.

Internal Joinery: The kitchen fittings are dated by present day standards, although generally satisfactory. Doors and skirting boards in the property are generally in a satisfactory condition, although some minor damage was noted which is in need of repair or replacement. The straight flight staircase is steep and a potential hazard.

Internal Decorations: Interior decorations are in a fair condition, generally habitable and adequate for occupation. Many buyers would wish to carry out internal redecoration after moving in.

Other: The cellar, positioned below the front reception room is of restricted use, having a relatively low head room and generally damp walls.

This is too subjectively reported here. If the ventilation to the floors is inadequate, it will need to be reported accordingly in Section E4 of the HCR.

ACTION items are not required in the HCR.

This is more of a future maintenance issue rather than an existing defect, so therefore would not be reported in the HCR.

Subjective opinion, therefore not required for the HCR.

In the HCR, this would be included at the beginning of Section E and reported as a restriction to inspection.

This comment would be too subjective for the HCR.

Although comments such as these help to put evidence into context, their focus is too subjective for the HCR.

This type of all encompassing caveat should not be included in the HCR.

As a potential hazard, this would need to be reported accordingly in Section C of the HCR.

Deficiency, therefore not reported in the HCR.

HOMEBUYER
THE RICS
SURVEY & VALUATION

THE SURVEY

6

As standard IEE advice will be included in the HCR, in this example there would be no need to call for a precautionary electrical test. In this case, all that would need to be reported in the HCR is a description of what the Home Inspector had seen.

D: THE SERVICES & SITE

The efficiency, compliance with regulations and adequacy of design of services can only be assessed by tests conducted by suitably qualified specialists. Although surveyors are not specialists in these particular areas, an informed opinion can be given on the basis of the accessible evidence. Where possible, drainage inspection-chambers are examined (except in the case of flats), but drains are not tested during the Inspection. However, in all cases advice is given if there is cause to suspect a problem. Leisure facilities and non-permanent outbuildings are noted but not examined.

PLEASE READ THESE NOTES

D1
THE SERVICES
- Electricity
- Gas
- Water
- Heating
- Other

D2
DRAINAGE

D3
THE SITE
- Garage and outbuildings
- Grounds and boundaries

Once again, as standard CORGI advice will be included in the HCR, there is no need to automatically call for a precautionary test.

ACTION items are not required in the HCR.

This comment is too subjective in the context of the HCR.

There is no requirement to report this type of deficiency in the HCR.

D1 THE SERVICES
Electricity: The property is connected to the mains electrical supply with a consumer unit located within the understair cupboard. The wiring system looks as if it has been upgraded in recent years. However, there are some trailing cables and surface wired cables within the loft cupboard and understair cupboard, and is unlikely to comply with modern regulations. You are advised to arrange for the system to be tested by an electrician as soon as possible after purchase as a precautionary measure.

Gas: The property is connected to the mains gas supply with the meter located in the cellar. Gas supply pipework where seen, is run in galvanised iron barrel pipework and in a general fair condition for its age. The meter is located in the cellar.

There is no special reason to anticipate a problem, but you are advised to arrange a full test by a CORGI approved contractor before taking up occupation.

Water: A stop cock is located within the cellar. Plumbing is old and incorporates some lead pipework. This is in need of upgrading.

ACTION: You are advised to obtain quotations for the necessary work. Please also see Section F1.

The sanitary fittings are in a generally fair condition, although a little dated with general wear and tear, and longer term replacement would be beneficial.

Heating: The Vaillant VCWCB242E combination boiler provides radiator central heating and domestic hot water to the property. The boiler, which is a balanced fan-flued system, probably installed during the early 1980s, is located on the side wall in the bathroom.

The heating system was turned off at the time of inspection.

The positioning of the boiler just above the bath is unusual and inconvenient. In the longer term, improvements to this arrangement would be beneficial.

You should check that as a minimum, the boiler and installation generally has been serviced on a regular basis. In the event that no recent service history can be demonstrated, we would strongly recommend that you have the boiler and system generally inspected by a CORGI engineer.

Other: We recommend that smoke detectors are provided to the property.

D2: DRAINAGE
Drainage we believe is connected into the public sewer via a system which may be shared with adjoining owners.

Access is by means of a single inspection chamber to the rear of the property in the rear garden, the lid to which we lifted and saw no signs of recent or significant blockage.

D3: THE SITE
Garage and Outbuildings: There is no garage, parking space, off-street parking, hard standing for a vehicle, or outbuildings.

Grounds and Boundaries: To the rear of the property the fencing is in a very poor condition and needs to be renewed. It is important, however, that you ask your conveyancer to check the boundaries against the title plan.

ACTION: You are advised to obtain quotations for the necessary work. Please also see Section F1.

In the rear garden there a small number of mature and semi-mature trees within and close to the boundaries of the property. Trees can potentially cause damage to structures and services, though no evidence was seen. They will need to be subject to pruning and general management in the future to restrict root and crown growth. This is particularly important, given the shrinkable clay nature of the sub-soils which are liable to seasonal variations that can cause structural movement by shrinkage or heave.

This comment is too subjective for the context of the HCR.

In the HCR, this should only be reported if such a shortcoming represents a hazard or a defect.

This should be reported as an issue to be pursued through the conveyancer's enquiries, in Section C of the HCR.

Advice in respect of trees and their potential influence on subsoils, building structures and services generally falls outside the scope of the HCR. However, if such issues represent a specific risk that lenders or others need to be made aware of, or there is evidence of structural damage caused by trees, they should be reported accordingly in Section B of the HCR.

HOMEBUYER THE SURVEY 7

E: LEGAL & OTHER MATTERS

PLEASE READ
THESE NOTES

E1
TENURE

E2
REGULATIONS,
etc.

E3
GUARANTEES,
etc.

E4
OTHER MATTERS

Your Legal Advisers are responsible for checking relevant documents relating to the Property (these might include servicing records and any guarantees, reports and specifications on previous repair works) as well as for carrying out all the standard searches and inquiries. However, if any specific matters are identified which the Legal Advisers should investigate on your behalf, these are reported in this section.

ACTION

You should IMMEDIATELY pass a copy of this Report to your Legal Advisers, asking them to check:

1. the standard searches and inquiries;
2. all the relevant items referred to in sub-sections E1–E4;
3. the assumptions made in arriving at the Market Value (which are itemised in the footnote to Section G1).

E1: TENURE
We understand that the property is to be sold freehold with vacant possession.

E2: REGULATIONS
You should ask your legal adviser to investigate and advise upon:
- Availability of Building Regulation Consents for the chimney breast alterations.

E3: GUARANTEES
You should ask your legal adviser to investigate and advise upon:
- Whether there are any guarantees in existence for the timber treatment and damp proofing works which have been carried out.

E4: OTHER MATTERS with legal implications
Your legal adviser should investigate and advise upon:
- The ownership of boundary walls and fences, and confirmation that these represent the legal boundaries.
- The extent of rights for you to enter on to adjacent properties to maintain any structures situated near or on the boundaries, and any similar rights that your neighbours may have to enter on to your property. The Party Wall etc. Act 1996 applies to this property.
- The Council Tax Band, which is understood to be Band C.

This issue does not need to be identified or included in the HCR.

HOMEBUYER SURVEY & VALUATION THE SURVEY 8

F: SUMMARY

Assuming that you decide to proceed with the purchase of this Property, there may be some things on which you should take action, such as obtaining competitive quotations for urgent repairs. (If any further investigation of some urgent matter is recommended, this will involve a second visit to the Property, perhaps by an appropriate specialist who will submit a separate report.)

ACTION

If, after reading and considering this Report, you intend to proceed with the purchase, or in Scotland make an offer, you should IMMEDIATELY pass a copy of this Report to your Legal Advisers – as advised in Section E. They will check (i) the standard searches and inquiries; (ii) all the relevant items covered in sub-sections E1-E4; and (iii) the assumptions made in arriving at Market Value.

Any ACTION recommendations made in Sections B, C and D are listed below under the relevant headings. In each case (if any), **I strongly advise you to obtain competitive quotations from reputable contractors at once.**

As soon as you have these, as well as the responses from your Legal Advisers, I will be pleased to advise you whether or not they would cause us to change the advice or Valuation given in this Report. Only when you have all this information will you be fully equipped to make an informed judgement on whether or not to proceed.

If you should decide to exchange contracts (or in Scotland, make an offer) without obtaining this information, you might have to accept the risk that some adverse factors might come to light after you are committed to the purchase.

The equivalent information will be displayed in the Summary of Ratings in Section B of the HCR, but will not include repair recommendations.

Urgent Repair:

You are recommended to treat the following as urgent repairs, to be remedied as soon as possible after purchase:
- C5: Rainwater Fittings: Overhaul (via building contractor)
- C5: Main Walls: Repairs (via building contractor)
- C5: External Joinery: Repairs (via building contractor)
- C5: External Decoration: Redecoration (via building contractor)
- C6: Floors: Ventilation (via building contractor)
- D1: Water: Plumbing Upgrade (via qualified contractor)
- D3: Grounds: Boundary Fence Repairs (via building contractor)

This information will be reported against a recommendation for investigation of observed defects in Section B of the HCR.

Further Investigation:

You are strongly advised to arrange for the following further investigations to be made and reported on before you exchange contracts:
- C2: Timber Defects (via timber/damp specialist)
- C3: Damp Repairs (via timber/damp specialist)

It is possible that the quotations for the work specified above may affect the valuation. You are therefore invited to contact the surveyor as soon as you receive this information. You can then be advised whether or not any change to the advice given in this report is required.

There is no requirement in the HCR for cost of works, or quotations to be included or sought. The impact on value on any such works identified will be irrelevant to the Home Inspector and not accounted for in the HCR.

F2: MAINTENANCE CONSIDERATIONS
In any building there are, of course, various standard maintenance matters which need attention from time to time. However, the following items have been noted which may involve significant future expenditure:
- C5: Chimneys
- C6: Ceilings
- C6: Internal Joinery

No issues of future maintenance need to be reported in the HCR.

F3: OTHER CONSIDERATIONS
No other significant considerations were noted.

HOMEBUYER SURVEY & VALUATION | **THE VALUATION** 9

G: VALUATION

**PLEASE READ
THESE NOTES**

In arriving at the opinion of the Property's Market Value as defined in Section D2 of the *Description of the HOMEBUYER Service* (attached), various assumptions* are made, subject to any change stated below. Legal Advisers, and others who undertake property conveyancing, should be familiar with the assumptions and are responsible for checking those concerning legal matters. *The opinion of the Market Value given below could be affected by the outcome of the inquiries by your Legal Advisers [Section E] and/or any further investigation and quotations for urgent repairs [Section F]. The Valuation assumes that your Legal Advisers will obtain satisfactory replies to their inquiries relating to the assumptions made in this Report.*

**GI
MARKET VALUE**

G1: MARKET VALUE
In our opinion, the market value of the freehold interest with vacant possession as at the 2nd December 2005, is in the region of £150,000 (one hundred and fifty thousand pounds).

**G2
INSURANCE
COVER
[REINSTATEMENT
COST]**

G2: INSURANCE COVER
The estimated cost of rebuilding the property is £147,000 (one hundred and forty seven thousand pounds).

The HCR has no requirement to provide an opinion on the property's market value.

- This Report is provided in accordance with the terms of the *Description of the HOMEBUYER Service* previously supplied, subject to any agreed addition noted below. (An additional copy is attached herewith.)

- The Report is solely for your use and your professional advisers', and no liability to anyone else is accepted. Should you not act upon advice contained in the Report, no responsiblity is accepted for the consequences.

- I hereby certify that the Property has been inspected by me and that I have prepared this Report, including the opinion of Market Value.

SIGNATURE

SURVEYOR'S NAME AND
PROFESSIONAL QUALIFICATIONS   JR HARTLEY FRICS

NAME AND ADDRESS OF
SURVEYOR'S ORGANISATION   HOME INSPECTORS.CO.UK LTD

DATE OF REPORT   2 DECEMBER 2005

AGREED ADDITION (IF ANY) TO   NONE
THE DESCRIPTION OF THE SERVICE

---

* Full details of these assumptions are available from the Surveyor. The most important are, in brief:

Concerning the materials, construction, services, fixtures and fittings, etc. that:
- No significant defects or cause to alter the Valuation would be revealed by an inspection of those parts which have not been inspected;
- No hazardous or damaging materials or building techniques have been used in the Property; there is no contamination in or from the ground; and the ground is not land-filled;
- The Property is connected to, and there is the right to use, the reported main services; and
- The Valuation takes no account of furnishings, removable fittings and sales incentives of any description.

Concerning legal matters, that:
- The Property is sold 'with vacant posssession';
- No laws are broken by the condition of the Property or by its present or intended use;
- The Property is not subject to any particularly troublesome or unusual restrictions; it is not affected by any problems which would be revealed by the usual legal inquiries; and all necessary planning permissions and building regulations consents (including consents for alterations) have been obtained and complied with; and
- The Property has the right to use the main services on normal terms; and the sewers, main services and roads giving access to the Property have been 'adopted' (i.e. are under local authority, not private, control).

HOME CONDITION REPORT

(Version 14 November 2005)

THE ROLE OF THE HOME INSPECTOR AND THE HOME CONDITION REPORT

INTRODUCTION & TERMS ON WHICH REPORT IS PREPARED

To sell your home you must have a home information pack that includes a home condition report. This home condition report is produced by a home inspector, who is licensed by (Scheme Name) (a government-approved certification scheme).

The home inspector has a duty to provide an objective opinion about the condition of the property which the buyer, the seller and the buyer's mortgage company can rely on and use.

To get a licence from (Scheme Name) a home inspector has to:

- pass an assessment of skills, in line with National Occupational Standards; and
- have insurance that covers negligence.

Home inspectors must follow the necessary standards and (Scheme Name's) code of conduct.

A home condition report is not valid unless it has been produced by a home inspector who is licensed by a government-approved scheme, and it has been entered on the Central Register of Home Condition Reports.

The home condition report is in a standard format and is based on these terms, which set out what you should expect of both the home inspector and the home condition report. Neither you nor the home inspector can amend these terms. Any further services the home inspector may provide are not covered by these terms and so must be covered by a separate contract.

If you have any complaint about this report, you can complain by following the complaints procedure, which is explained in more detail at the end of this document.

WHAT THIS REPORT TELLS YOU

This report tells you:

- about the construction and condition of the home on the date it was inspected; and
- if necessary, whether further enquiries or investigations are needed.

The report's main aim is to tell you about defects that need urgent attention or are serious. It also tells you about things that need further investigation to prevent damage to the structure of the building and are on a set list of threats to personal safety.

The report gives 'condition ratings' to the major parts of the main building (it does not give condition ratings to outbuildings). However, the report does not mention minor defects that do not need building work to put them right.

The report contains an energy performance certificate that tells you about the energy and environmental performance of the home and suggests improvements that you can make.

WHAT THIS REPORT DOES NOT TELL YOU

This report does not tell you:

- the value of your home or cover things that are more specifically considered when a valuation is provided, such as the locality of the home or the availability of public transport or facilities
- It does not tell you about any minor defects that would not normally have any effect on a buyer's decision to buy.

- This report does not warn you about any health and safety risks to people using or visiting the property, unless the risks are such that repair or building work is needed. The report does not contain advice on the cost of any repair work or the methods of repair which should be used.

The report is not an asbestos inspection within the meaning of the Control of Asbestos at Work Regulations 2002.

A seller, buyer or lender who needs advice on subjects that are not covered by the home condition report must arrange for it to be provided separately.

WHAT IS INSPECTED?

The home inspector inspects the inside and outside of the main building and all permanent outbuildings, and the visible parts of the services, gas, electricity, water and drainage services.

The inspector gives each part of the structure of the main building a condition rating, to make the report easy to follow. The Condition Ratings are as follows:

CONDITION RATING	DEFINITION
Not inspected	Not inspected.
1	No repair is currently needed. Normal maintenance must be carried out.
2	Repairs or replacements are needed but the home inspector does not consider these to be serious or urgent.
3	These are defects which are either serious and/or require urgent repair or replacement.

IMPORTANT NOTE

The inspection is 'non-invasive'. This means that the home inspector does not take up carpets, floor coverings or floorboards, move furniture or remove the contents of cupboards. Also, the home inspector does not remove secured panels or undo electrical fittings.

The home inspector will say at the start of sections D, E and F of the report where it was not possible to inspect any parts of the home that are normally reported on.

Where the home inspector has reason to be concerned about these parts, the report will tell you about any further investigations that are needed. The home inspector does not report on the cost of any remedial work or how repairs should be carried out.

SECTION A

GENERAL INFORMATION

HOME CONDITION REPORT

Address of the property that has been inspected:

> 121 Victorian Villas
> Piketown-on-Sea
> Pikeshire, MM1 1MN

Property reference number (if known):

> 987655

Home inspector's name:

> JR Hartley

Home inspector's licence number:

> 012345

Company name:

> Home Inspectors.co.uk Ltd

Company address and postcode:

> 1 High Street
> Tenchtown
> Pikeshire, MM1 2SS

Company email address:

> JRH@homeinspectors.co.uk

Company telephone number:

> 002020202020202

Company fax number:

> 002020202020201

Date of the inspection:

> 5th December 2005

Report Reference Number:

> 9098765433

The Report Reference Number(s) of Home condition reports written for this property in the last 12 months:

> 0

Disclosure on Related Parties*

> Not applicable

NOTE: Statements e.g. 'Date of the inspection' will appear on the public version. However, questions, (identified in brackets) are prompts for completion of the form but will not appear on the public version.

SECTION B

SUMMARY

Date of the inspection:
| 5th December 2005 |

Full address and postcode of the property:
| 121 Victorian Villas
Piketown-on-Sea
Pikeshire, MM1 1MN |

Weather conditions:
| The weather at the time of inspection was dry. |

The state of property when inspected.
(Was the property furnished or unfurnished?)
| The property was vacant and unfurnished. |

Approximated year of construction
(When was the property built?)
| 1880 |

Approximate year when the property was
extended. (When was the extension built?)
| The rear extension was built in 1950. |

When was the property converted?

Type of property:
| The property is a mid-terraced house. |

Are there any signs of tenants living in the property?
| |

Is the property in an area occupied primarily
by tenants?
| No |

Is the property in a conservation area or likely
to be listed?
Listing grade (if known):
| |

For Flats and Maisonettes

Position of the flat in the block
(Which floor is the flat on and how many floors
are there in the block?)
(Number of flats in the block?)

(Is the property purpose-built or converted?)

(Is there a lift to the flat?)

(What commercial uses are there within the block?)
(What percentage of the building has
commercial use?)
(Where in the building is the commercial use?)

(Since the property is a terraced house, the above fields will not appear on the final report.)

Accommodation

Storey	Living Rooms	Bed-rooms	Bath and/ or shower	Separate WC	Kitchen	Utility Room	Conservatory (hot or cold)	Other	Name of 'Other'
Lower Ground									
Ground	2			1	1				
First		2	1						
Second									
Third									
Fourth									
Roof space									
Totals	2	2	1	1	1	0	0	0	

House only: Gross external floor area (m²) | 120 | Reinstatement Cost | £147,000

Flat only: Gross internal floor area (m²) | –

Note: This reinstatement cost is the estimated cost of completely rebuilding the property. It represents the sum at which the home should be insured against fire and other risks. It is based on building and other related costs and does not include the value of the land the home is built on. It does not include leisure facilities such as swimming pools and tennis courts. The figure should be reviewed regularly as building costs change. **Importantly, it is not a valuation of the property.**

If the property is very large or historic, or if it incorporates special features or is of unusual construction and a specialist would be needed to assess the reinstatement cost, no cost figure is provided and the report says that a specialist is needed.

Construction

A short general description of the construction

> The roofs to the property are covered by tile and the walls are of brick.
> The floors are of mixed timber and solid construction, and the windows are of mixed timber casement, double-hung sash and louvre style.

(Is the property of system built construction?)
(If it is please advise the name of the system)

(These two boxes will not appear on the report.)

Mains Services

The ticked boxes indicate that mains services are connected

Drainage	Gas	Electricity	Water
✓	✓	✓	✓

If no drainage, gas, electricity or water is provided, please say what services there are. (This is a prompt box and will not appear on the public report.)	

Central Heating

(Does the property have central heating?)	Yes
(Type of fuel)	Gas
(Full or partial system)	Full

(These are prompt boxes that will not appear on the report.)

Outside Facilities

(Is a garage provided?)	No
(Is the garage on or off the site?)	
(Is the garage part of the building?)	
(Is the garage a single, double or more?)	
(Is there a carport?)	No
(Number of allocated parking spaces?)	
(Are these on or off the site?)	
(Are there any gardens which are part of the property?)	Yes
(Are the gardens to the front, side or back?)	There is no front garden as the property opens directly onto the pavement from the entrance hall. There is a small rear garden.
(Are there any outbuildings with the property?) (Number of outbuildings?)	There are no permanent outbuildings.
(How the outbuildings are used)	
(Are the roads and footpaths made up?)	Yes

(Fields that are not relevant to the subject property will not appear in the final report.)

Summary of Ratings

(This is generated by the system from the information the inspector provides.)

Section of the Report	Part Number	Part Name	Identifier (if there is more than one entry in the table)	Rating
D: Outside condition	D1	Chimney stacks	A) Left hand chimney stack B) Rear chimney stack	A) 1 B) 2
	D2	Roof coverings	X	2
	D3	Rain water pipes & gutters	X	2
	D4	Main walls and claddings	A) Original building B) Rear extension C) Damp proof course	A) 2 B) 1 C) 3
	D5	Windows	X	2
	D6	External doors	X	2
	D7	All other woodwork	X	1
	D8	Outside decoration	X	2
	D9	Other outside detail	X	–
E: Inside condition	E1	Roof structure	X	2
	E2	Ceilings	X	2
	E3	Internal walls, partitions & plasterwork	X	2
	E4	Floors	X	2
	E5	Fireplaces & chimney breasts (and the outside of flues)	A) Living room B) Front bedroom C) Elsewhere	A) 2 B) 2 C) 1
	E6	Built-in fittings	X	1
	E7	Inside woodwork (staircase, joinery, etc.)	X	2
	E8	Bathroom fittings	X	1
	E9	Dampness	X	3
	E10	Other issues	X	–
F: Services	F1	Electricity	X	2
	F2	Gas/Oil	X	1
	F3	Water	X	2
	F4	Heating	X	2
	F5	Drainage	X	1

Overall condition of the property	Parts of the property are in a poor condition and require extensive repair.
Widespread problems that affect many parts of the property.	
Summary of structural movement	There is movement cracking and bowing to the outer walls in particular, and gapping around window and door openings, but I saw no evidence to suggest this is ongoing.

Further Investigation

Recommended investigation of defects seen or suspected:	Your attention is drawn to the following matter for which further investigation is recommended by someone who is appropriately qualified: ● Dampness and timber defects (Section E9)

SECTION C

CONVEYANCING AND HEALTH & SAFETY ISSUES

ISSUES FOR CONVEYANCERS

The home inspector does not act as 'the conveyancer'. However, if during the inspection, the inspector identifies issues that the conveyancers advising the buyer and seller may need to investigate further, the inspector will refer to these in the report. This is to draw the issues to the attention of others to improve the quality of the information in the home information pack. The inspector will not have seen the legal and other documents in the home information pack.

The conveyancer should investigate the issues below:

Roads and footpaths	
Drainage	The property has a shared drainage system situated outside the boundaries.
Water	
Planning and any other permission needed	The property has been altered by the removal of chimney breasts and the construction of a rear extension (now forming the cloakroom and rear entrance lobby) which may have required statutory consents.
Freehold owner consents	
Flying freeholds	
Mining	
Rights of way	
Boundaries (including Party Walls)	
Easements	
Repairs to shared parts	
Previous structural repairs	I understand that certain works including timber and damp treatment has been carried out to the property under warranty or guarantee.
New building warranties	
Building insurance (ongoing claims)	
Tree preservation orders	
Property let	

DANGEROUS MATERIALS AND CONTAMINATED LAND, SUBSIDENCE AND FLOODING

The home inspector assumes that:

- The home is not built with nor contains hazardous materials; and it is not built on contaminated land. However, if any of these materials are found during the inspection, or if the home inspector finds evidence to suspect that the land may be contaminated, this will be shown on the report along with recommendations for further investigations.

Contamination	
Subsidence	
Flooding	

HEALTH AND SAFETY RISKS

The home inspector will draw your attention to items from a set list of health and safety issues if they are seen at the property.

   The inspector does not have to identify risks which have existed in the property for a long time, and which cannot reasonably be changed. As an example, the inspector will not draw your attention to uneven floor surfaces that have existed for decades.

- The lack of windows that are easy to escape from at first floor level increases the risk of being trapped in the event of fire.
- The risk of injury is increased by the lack of safety glass in the rear door.
- The lack of fire doors between the entrance hall and kitchen increases the risk of being trapped in the event of fire.
- The unusually steep staircase is a safety risk.
- There are lead water pipes at the home. You should seek the advice of the local Water Authority on whether this poses a health risk in this locality.
- No evidence is available to confirm the recent testing and servicing of the boiler. Failure to test and service increases safety risks.
- No evidence is available to confirm the recent testing of the electrical installation. Failure to test and service increases safety risks.

SECTION D

OUTSIDE CONDITION

The inspector carried out a non-invasive inspection (see the important note at the beginning of this report for an explanation of 'non-invasive') of the outside of the main building and permanent outbuildings. They made this inspection from various points within the boundaries of the property and from public areas such as footpaths and open spaces, using binoculars where necessary. The inspector did not stand on walls or enter neighbouring private property. They examined roofs, chimneys and other external surfaces of the building from the ground. They inspected flat roofs to single-storey buildings from a ladder, where the surface of the roof was not more than three-metres above ground level. They did not inspect features above this level that cannot be seen from any point. Because of the risk of causing damage, the inspector did not walk on flat roofs. They assessed rainwater fittings (gutters and downpipes) only if there was heavy rain at the time of inspection.

The inspector looked at the overall condition and the state of repair of the outside parts of the property. The report does not reflect every minor blemish and does not point out each individual minor defect in the outside walls. However, where there are so many minor defects that together they are serious, the report will say this.

FLATS: OUTSIDE INSPECTION

When inspecting blocks of flats, it is often difficult to see the whole outside of a building or block, and its maintenance is rarely the responsibility of one person. The inspector only carried out a non-invasive inspection to the level of detail set out above, to the main walls, windows and roof over the flat.

The inspector did not inspect the rest of the block to this level of detail; but instead has formed an opinion based on a general inspection of the rest of the block. They provide information about the outside and shared parts so that the conveyancer can check whether the maintenance clauses in the lease or other title documents are adequate.

The inspector inspected the shared access to the flat together with the area where car parking and any garage for the flat are, along with the access to that area. They did not inspect other shared parts, such as separate halls, stairs and access ways to other flats in the block, the lift motor room and cleaning cupboards.

I could not inspect the (describe), because (………………..).

(The above field will not appear in the final report.)

D1 CHIMNEY STACKS	
Identifying name for the part (where more than one is recorded.)	A) Left hand chimney stack B) Rear chimney stack
Condition Rating	A) Left hand chimney stack – 1 B) Rear chimney stack – 2
Justification for Rating and Comments	The chimney stacks are of brick. The brickwork and cementwork to the rear stack is cracked and eroded. This requires repair or replacement, but is not considered serious or urgent.

SECTION D (continued)

D2 ROOF COVERINGS	
Identifying name for the part (where more than one is recorded.)	–
Condition Rating	2
Justification for Rating and Comments	The main and back addition roofs are sloping and covered with interlocking concrete tiles. The tiles in places have slipped and have lifted. This requires repair or replacement, but is not considered serious or urgent.

D3 RAIN WATER PIPES & GUTTERS	
Identifying name for the part (where more than one is recorded.)	–
Condition Rating	2
Justification for Rating and Comments	The rainwater fittings are of plastic. The gutter, in particular to the rear addition, adjacent to the boiler flue outlet is damaged and out of alignment. The gutters, in particular to the rear addition have become blocked with moss and debris. The rear gully is also blocked with debris. This requires repair or replacement, but is not considered serious or urgent.

D4 MAIN WALLS & CLADDINGS	
Identifying name for the part (where more than one is recorded.)	A) Original building B) Rear extension C) Damp proof course
Condition Rating	A) Original building – 2 B) Rear extension – 1 C) Damp proof course – 3
Justification for Rating and Comments	The walls to the original building are 225–350mm thick and are of solid construction, mainly brick, with part rendered and colour washed facings. The walls to the rear extension are 120mm thick and are of single skin construction. There are brick parapets adjacent to the main and addition roofs. A) The pointing to the original building, in particular around the window and door openings is missing or damaged. The brickwork is generally stained. This requires repair or replacement, but is not considered serious or urgent. B) No repair is presently required. Normal maintenance must be undertaken. C) The damp proof course, in particular to the rear main wall and the back addition is bridged and causing damp penetration. This is considered serious and in need of urgent repair or replacement.

SECTION D (continued)

D5 WINDOWS	
Identifying name for the part (where more than one is recorded.)	–
Condition Rating	2
Justification for Rating and Comments	The windows are a mixture of casement, double hung sash and louvre style timber. The window sills at the front of the building are stone.
	The louvre windows are draughty and rotten. The remaining window joints are rotten, loose and damaged. The stone window sills at the front of the building at first floor level are damaged. This requires repair or replacement, but is not considered serious or urgent.

D6 EXTERNAL DOORS	
Identifying name for the part (where more than one is recorded.)	–
Condition Rating	2
Justification for Rating and Comments	The external doors are of glazed timber.
	The front door is swollen and difficult to open. The rear door is badly fitting.
	This requires repair or replacement, but is not considered serious or urgent.

D7 ALL OTHER WOODWORK	
Identifying name for the part (where more than one is recorded.)	–
Condition Rating	1
Justification for Rating and Comments	The external woodwork includes painted softwood roof eaves. No repair is presently required.

SECTION D (continued)

D8 OUTSIDE DECORATION	
Identifying name for the part (where more than one is recorded.)	–
Condition Rating	2
Justification for Rating and Comments	Decorated areas include the exterior doors, windows and roof eaves. The decorations are incomplete, faded, peeling and blistered, resulting in rot to the windows in particular. This requires repair or replacement, but is not considered serious or urgent.

D9 OTHER OUTSIDE DETAIL	
Identifying name for the part (where more than one is recorded.)	There are no other external details.
Condition Rating	–
Justification for Rating and Comments	–

SECTION E

INSIDE CONDITION

The home inspector carried out a non-invasive inspection of all the parts of the home they could see without causing damage. However, if the inspector could not see a part of the home without the risk of damage, and they suspect that there could be a problem, the report will say this and include recommendations on the need for further investigation.

The home inspector checked for damp in vulnerable areas by using a moisture-measuring meter.

They inspected the roof structure from inside the roof space where it was accessible but did not move or lift insulation material, stored goods and other contents. The inspector did not walk around the space if there was a risk to safety (for example, where insulation covers the ceiling joists); instead they inspected the roof from the access point.

They opened some of the windows and all the doors, they inspected floor surfaces and under-floor spaces where they were readily accessible, they did not move or lift furniture, floor coverings or other contents. The home inspector has not commented on sound insulation or chimney flues (or both), because it is rarely practical to do so without using specialist equipment that home inspectors do not carry.

> I could not inspect the ground floor back addition roof space because there was no access trap.

E1 ROOF STRUCTURE	
Identifying name for the part (where more than one is recorded.)	–
Condition Rating	2
Justification for Rating and Comments	The main and rear addition roof frames are constructed of cut softwood timber.
	The chimney breast has been partly removed, but has been supported on steel brackets. The roof timbers are stained, split and infested by wood boring beetle. This requires repair or replacement, but is not considered serious or urgent.

E2 CEILINGS	
Identifying name for the part (where more than one is recorded.)	–
Condition Rating	2
Justification for Rating and Comments	The ceilings are a mixture of lath and plaster, plasterboard and hardboard.
	The ceilings are affected by cracking. The lath and plaster ceilings are generally uneven. The ceiling in the kitchen is distorted and damaged. This requires repair or replacement, but is not considered serious or urgent.

SECTION E (continued)

E3 INTERNAL WALLS, PARTITIONS & PLASTERWORK	
Identifying name for the part (where more than one is recorded.)	–
Condition Rating	2
Justification for Rating and Comments	The internal walls and partitions are a mixture of solid and lightweight timber construction, most of which is lath and plaster or plasterboard faced.
	The internal walls are affected by cracking. The plaster, in particular in the entrance hall is damaged and damp, and elsewhere is hollow, uneven and incomplete. The ceramic wall tiling in the kitchen is damaged. This requires repair or replacement, but is not considered serious or urgent.

E4 FLOORS	
Identifying name for the part (where more than one is recorded.)	–
Condition Rating	2
Justification for Rating and Comments	The floors are a mixture of suspended timber and solid construction.
	The timber floors in particular to the living room are springy, uneven, affected by wood boring beetle and have been strengthened following rot damage. The floors, in particular to the front and rear reception rooms are inadequately ventilated. This requires repair or replacement, but is not considered serious or urgent.

E5 FIREPLACES & CHIMNEY BREASTS (AND THE OUTSIDE OF FLUES)	
Identifying name for the part (where more than one is recorded.)	A) Living room B) Front bedroom C) Elsewhere
Condition Rating	A) Living room – 2 B) Front bedroom – 2 C) Elsewhere – 1
Justification for Rating and Comments	The chimney breasts are of mainly brick construction with a plaster finish. The chimney breasts in the rear bedroom, the dining room and in the roof space have been removed.
	The fireplace opening in the front bedroom is blocked and is inadequately ventilated. The fire surround to the living room is stained. This requires repair or replacement, but is not considered serious or urgent.

SECTION E (continued)

E6 BUILT-IN FITTINGS	
Identifying name for the part (where more than one is recorded.)	–
Condition Rating	1
Justification for Rating and Comments	The built-in fittings including kitchen fitments and wardrobes are a mixture of softwood and medium density fibreboard (commonly known as MDF). The kitchen fitments are dated and there is damage and staining. No repair is presently required, but normal maintenance must be undertaken.

E7 INSIDE WOODWORK (STAIRCASE, JOINERY, ETC.)	
Identifying name for the part (where more than one is recorded.)	–
Condition Rating	2
Justification for Rating and Comments	The internal woodwork including doors, skirtings, bannisters and staircases are of mainly softwood construction. The dining room and kitchen doors are missing and may provide inadequate protection in the event of fire. The fanlights at first floor level are broken. Skirtings, in particular in the kitchen are partly missing or affected by rot. This requires repair or replacement, but is not considered serious or urgent.

E8 BATHROOM FITTINGS	
Identifying name for the part (where more than one is recorded.)	–
Condition Rating	1
Justification for Rating and Comments	The sanitary fittings in the bathroom comprise a pressed steel panelled bath, low level ceramic WC and ceramic wash hand basin. The cloakroom has been set up as a 'wet-room' and comprises a ceramic low level WC with plastic cistern, together with a shower which has been disconnected in the past. The fittings are worn, stained and dated. Seals around the fittings in the bathroom are faulty. No repair is presently required, but normal maintenance must be undertaken.

SECTION E (continued)

E9 DAMPNESS	
Identifying name for the part (where more than one is recorded.)	–
Condition Rating	3
Justification for Rating and Comments	There is evidence of a chemical injection damp proof course to the front, rear and back addition walls, together with a partial remedial polythene damp proof course visible from within the cellar.

Penetrating/rising dampness is affecting the property, in particular the kitchen, living room and dining room at ground floor level. This is likely to have been caused by high ground levels, bridged damp proof course and inadequate external surface water drainage.

Penetrating dampness and condensation is affecting the underground walls in the cellar, likely to have been caused by lack of damp proof membrane. Further advice should be obtained. |

E10 OTHER ISSUES	
Identifying name for the part (where more than one is recorded.)	There are no other internal issues.
Condition Rating	–
Justification for Rating and Comments	–

SECTION F

SERVICES

Services are generally hidden within the construction of the property; for example, pipes are beneath the floors and wiring is within the walls. As a result only the visible parts of the available services can be inspected. Specialist tests were not carried out. The visual inspection does not assess the services to make sure they work properly and efficiently and meet modern standards. If any services (such as the boiler or mains water) are turned off, the home inspector will state that in the report and will not turn them on.

Otherwise, the home inspector turned on some taps on appliances and, where safe and practical to do so, lifted the covers on the drainage inspection chambers. The home inspector reports only on the services covered in this section (electricity, gas, oil, water, heating and drainage). All other services and domestic appliances are not included in the reporting: for example, security and door-answering systems, smoke alarms, television, cable, wireless and satellite communication systems, cookers, hobs, washing machines and fridges (even where built-in). The report gives some general advice on safety and the importance of maintaining the services in the home.

The (describe service) was (describe):

(The above field will not appear in the final report.)

F1 ELECTRICITY	
General Advice endorsed by the Institute of Electrical Engineers	*Safety Warning: Periodic inspection and testing of electrical installations is important to protect your home from damage and to ensure the safety of the occupants. Guidance published by the Institute of Electrical Engineers recommends that inspections and testing are undertaken at least every 10 years and on change of occupancy.* *All electrical installation work undertaken after 1st January 2005 should be identified by an Electrical Installation Certificate.*
Condition Rating	2
Justification for Rating and Comments	There is a mains electricity supply and the meter is located in the understairs cupboard. The cables, in particular to the understair cupboard are trailing and poorly clipped. The old style radiant heater in the bathroom is dated and of a poor quality. This requires repair or replacement, but is not considered serious or urgent.

SECTION F (continued)

F2 GAS/OIL	
General Advice endorsed by CORGI (Council of Registered Gas Installers)	*Safety Warning: Regular servicing of the gas installation and all gas appliances is important to ensure you protect your home from damage and to ensure the safety of the occupants. This MUST be carried out by a CORGI registered installer. If there is no current certificate relating to an appliance installation, a CORGI registered installer should check and test the installation.*
General Advice endorsed by OFTEC (Oil Firing Technical Association)	*Safety Warning: Periodic inspection and testing of equipment connected with oil installations is important to protect your home and environment and to reduce risks from fire, carbon monoxide poisoning and pollution from leaks. Full advice can be obtained from OFTEC.*
Condition Rating	1
Justification for Rating and Comments	There is a mains gas supply and the meter is located in the cellar. No repair is presently required, but normal maintenance must be undertaken.

F3 WATER	
Condition Rating	2
Justification for Rating and Comments	The water pipework is a mixture of copper and lead, and the stopcock is located in the cellar. The pipework, in particular in the understair cupboard and kitchen is poorly supported. This requires repair or replacement, but is not considered serious or urgent.

F4 HEATING	
Condition Rating	2
Justification for Rating and Comments	Heating and hot water are provided by a gas wall-hung combination boiler located in the bathroom. Some of the radiators are rusty and damaged. This requires repair or replacement, but is not considered serious or urgent.

F5 DRAINAGE	
Condition Rating	1
Justification for Rating and Comments	There is a mains drainage system. Surface water is combined with the foul drainage system. No repair is presently required, but normal maintenance must be undertaken.

SECTION G

GROUNDS

The home inspector inspected the condition of the boundary walls, outbuildings and shared facilities.

To inspect these areas the home inspector walked around the grounds. The report provides a summary of the general condition of any garden walls, fences, and permanent outbuildings. Conservatories with translucent or clear roofs attached to the main buildings are treated as outbuildings, as are garages and permanent store sheds. Buildings containing swimming pools and sports facilities are also treated as outbuildings, but the home inspector does not report on the leisure facilities, such as the pool itself and its equipment.

The inspector did not inspect leisure facilities, landscaping and other facilities, including swimming pools and tennis courts, and non-permanent outbuildings.

(Comments on garages)	
(Comments on permanent sheds)	
(Comments on other permanent outbuildings)	
(Comments on boundary walls)	The boundary walls at the rear are of brick construction. This requires repair or replacement, but is not considered serious or urgent.
(Comments on other walls)	
(Comments on paved areas)	Pavings are uneven and breaking up in places.
(Comments on shared facilities)	
(Comments on detached conservatories)	
(Comments on other structures)	

(Fields that are not relevant to the subject property will not appear in the final report.)

SECTION H

ENERGY PERFORMANCE CERTIFICATE

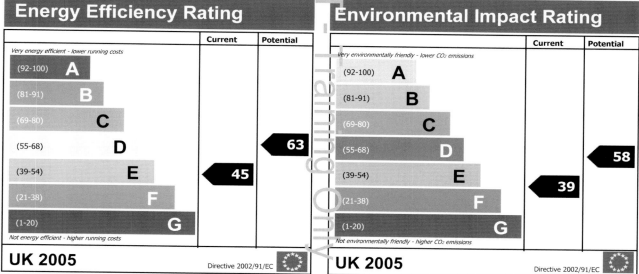

Section H: Energy Performance Certificate
Save money, improve comfort and help the environment

The following report is based on an inspection carried out for:

Address:
121, Victorian Villas,
Piketown-on-sea,
Pikeshire, MM1 1MN

Building type: Home
Whole or part: Whole
Methodology: RDSAP
Inspection date: 5/12/2005

Certif. Number:
Date issued:
Inspector name:

This home's performance ratings

This home has been inspected and its performance rated in terms of its energy efficiency and environmental impact. This is calculated using the UK Standard Assessment Procedure (SAP) for dwellings which gives you an energy efficiency rating based on fuel cost and an environmental impact rating based on carbon dioxide (CO_2) emissions.

Energy Efficiency Rating

Current: 45, Potential: 63

Environmental Impact Rating

Current: 39, Potential: 58

The energy efficiency rating is a measure of the overall efficiency of a home. The higher the rating the more energy efficient the home is and the lower the fuel bills will be.

The environmental impact rating is a measure of this home's impact on the environment. The higher the rating the less impact it has on the environment.

Typical fuel costs and carbon dioxide (CO2) emissions of this home

This table provides you with an indication of how much it will cost to provide lighting, heating and hot water to this home. The fuel costs and carbon dioxide emissions are calculated based on a SAP assessment of the actual energy use that would be needed to deliver the defined level of comfort in this home, using standard occupancy assumptions, which are described on page 4. The energy use includes the energy used in producing and delivering the fuels to this home. The fuel costs only take into account the cost of fuel and not any associated service, maintenance or safety inspection costs. The costs have been provided for guidance only as it is unlikely they will match actual costs for any particular household.

	Current	Potential
Energy use	39,307 kWh/m2 per year	24,269 kWh/m2 per year
Carbon dioxide emissions	7.9 tonnes per year	5.0 tonnes per year
Lighting	£74 per year	£61 per year
Heating	£538 per year	£306 per year
Hot water	£83 per year	£69 per year

To see how this home's performance ratings can be improved please go to page 2

Section H: Energy Performance Certificate

Summary of this home's energy performance related features

The table shows the current performance of each element of this home on the following scale:
Extremely poor/ Very poor/ Poor/ Average/ Good/ Very good/ Excellent

Element	Description	Current performance
Main walls	SO Solid Brick:, Insulation: A As Built, Solid U: 2.10	???
Main roof	P Pitched, Insulation at: J Joists, Thickness: 100 mm	???
Main floor	U: 1.79 A: 57.21 m2	???
Windows	N Normal, Doble Glazed: 0%	???
Main heating	AABC	???
Main heating controls	CBC Program and/or roomstat (NBO)	???
Secondary heating	JAA Efficiency: 50.00%	???
Hot water	HWP From the primary heating system	???
Lighting	Rooms: 7, L.E.L. Fittings: 0, External lights: None	???

Current energy efficiency rating	**E 45**
Current environmental impact rating	**E 39**

Measures to improve this home's performance ratings

The improved energy ratings are cumulative, that is they assume the improvements have been installed in the order that they appear in the table.

Lower cost measures	Typical savings	Energy rating after improvement
Draughtproof all doors and windows	£20	E 46
Solid wall add 50mm (2 inches) insulation	£110	E 54
Sub Total	£130	
Higher cost measures		
Fit thermostatic radiator valves	£23	D 56
Replace boiler with fully controlled gas condensing combi boiler for heating and hot water	£70	D 62
Sub Total	£93	

Potential energy efficiency rating	**D 63**
Potential environmental impact rating	**D 58**

Further measures to achieve even higher standards

Double glaze the single glazed windows	£22	D 63

Enhanced energy efficiency rating	**D 63**
Enhanced environmental impact rating	**D 65**

Improvements to the energy efficiency and environmental impact ratings will usually be in step with each other. However, they can sometimes diverge because reduced energy costs are very occasionally not accompanied by reduced carbon dioxide emissions.

Section H: Energy Performance Certificate

Measures to reduce the running costs and improve this home's energy ratings

Lower cost measures (typically up to £500 each)

These improvements are relatively cheap to install and will be worth tackling first.

Measure 1
Cavity wall
The external walls of your home are built with a gap, called a cavity, between the inside and outside layers of the wall. Cavity wall insulation fills this gap with an insulating material. The material is pumped into the gap through small holes, which are drilled into the outside layer of the walls (the small holes are sealed up afterwards). Because this involves using specialist machinery, a professional installation company must carry out the work. The contractor will thoroughly survey your walls before commencing work to be sure that this type of insulation is right for your home, and provide a guarantee for the work.

Measure 2
Topping up loft insulation
The anticipated cost is based upon a contractor installing an additional 100mm of glass fibre or mineral wool insulation in your loft, but it can also be installed by a capable DIY enthusiast. If you choose a DIY installation then take care not to block ventilation at the edge of the loft space as this may cause condensation. When handling the insulation always wear gloves and a mask.

Measure 3
Hot water and pipe insulation
Improving the insulation of your hot water tank using a very thick jacket will help reduce your heating bills. You should also insulate the hot water pipe connections to the cylinder, for about a metre, or as far as you can get access to them. Fit the jacket over the top of any existing jacket and over any thermostat clamped to the cylinder.

Higher cost measures (typically up to £3000 each)

Measure 4
Condensing boiler
This improvement is most appropriate when your existing central heating boiler needs repair or replacement. A condensing boiler is capable of much higher efficiencies than other types of boiler, meaning it will burn less fuel to heat your property. Only a qualified heating engineer should carry out the installation. [Building Regulations apply to this work, so you should get advice from your local Building Control Authority].

Measure 5
Installation of full controls package
Although your heating sytem already has a room thermostat, you can save more money by adding thermostatic radiator valves as well. They allow you to control the temperature of each room to suit your needs, adding to comfort and reducing your bills. For example, you can set them to be warmer in your living room and bathroom than in your bedrooms. You will need a plumber to fit them to every radiator except one - the radiator in the same room as your room thermostat. You still need the room thermostat, because without it, even when the TRVs have turned off the radiators, the boiler is still burning fuel and wasting your money - so don't let the plumber remove it.

Further measures to achieve an even higher standard

These measures should be considered if aiming for the highest possible standard for this home.

Measure 6
Double glazing
Replacing the existing single glazed windows with double-glazing will improve your comfort in your home by reducing draughts and cold spots near windows. This will also help to save on your heating bills during the long winter months. Building Regulations apply to this work, so you should either use a contractor who is registered with Fensa or get advice from your local Building Control Authority.

Measure 7
Solar water heating
Energy from the sun can be harnessed to provide domestic hot water. These systems do not generally provide space heating, and are described as 'Solar Thermal' systems. They are among the most cost effective renewable energy systems that can be installed on dwellings in urban or rural environments.

Section H: Energy Performance Certificate

About this energy inspection

Energy inspections are not new. They have been available in the UK since the late 1980's. Your inspection has been undertaken by a qualified inspector who has been trained to collect the correct information about the energy efficiency of your home. This information has been processed by a Government approved organisation to produce the energy rating and suggestions in the report. Both the inspector and the energy report supplier are regularly monitored to show that their work is up to standard.

If you would like clarification of the technical information in this energy report please contact the:

Inspector Stuart Fairlie on 01788 833 386

Inspector Registration Number   1000-0009

About this home's performance ratings

The ratings provide you with a measure of the overall energy efficiency of this home and its environmental impact. Both are calculated using the Standard Assessment Procedure (SAP), which is the Government's recommended system of assessing the energy efficiency of dwellings. The ratings take into account the home's insulation, heating systems, hot water system, fixed lighting, ventilation, number of windows and related fuels.

Not all of us use our homes in the same way so to allow one home to be directly compared to another, energy ratings are calculated using 'standard occupancy' assumptions. Standard occupancy assumes that the house is heated for 9 hours a day during weekdays and 16 hours a day at weekends, with the living room heated to 21°C and the rest of the house at 18°C.

The ratings are expressed on a scale of 1 to 100. The higher the energy efficiency rating the more energy efficient the home and the higher the environmental impact rating the less impact it has on the environment.

Homes which are more energy efficient use less energy, saving money and helping to protect the environment. A home with an energy efficiency rating of 100 would be energy self sufficient and so the cost of providing lighting, heating and hot water would be practically zero.

The potential rating shown on page one is the economic potential of the home assuming all cost effective measures have been installed. A home built to the 2005 Building Regulations would typically be at the boundary of bands B and C.

This home's impact on the environment

Carbon dioxide is one of the biggest contributors to the man-made greenhouse effect. The energy we use to heat, light and power our homes produces 28 per cent of the UK's CO_2 emissions.

The average household in the UK creates about six tonnes of CO_2 every year. There are simple steps you can take to cut CO_2 emissions and help prevent climate change. Making your home more energy efficient by adopting the suggestions in this report can help protect the environment by saving CO_2. You could save even more CO_2 by switching to renewable energy sources.

What can I do today?

In addition to the specific measures suggested in this report, don't forget there are many simple measures you can put into action today that will save you money and help reduce your impact on the environment.

For example:

- Check that your heating system thermostat is not set too high (21°C in the living room is suggested)
- Make sure your hot water is not too hot (60°C is suggested)
- Turn off your lights and domestic appliances when not needed, and do not leave TVs and videos on standby
- Do not overfill kettles and saucepans, and use a lid where possible
- Buy energy saving recommended appliances
- Find out if you are eligible for grants or offers to help with the cost of energy saving measures by visiting **www.est.org.uk/myhome** or calling **0800 512 012**.

Home Inspector's signature: .... (*Note: Facsimile signature taken from in the database*)

Home Inspector's Licence Number: ....

Name: ....

Qualifications: ....

Address: ....

....

....

....

Telephone Number: ....

Fax Number: ....

Email Address: ....

Date of making the report: ....

WHEN THE REPORT IS COMPLETE

All home condition reports are held on an electronic register run by (state name). You can see a copy of this report online at (www.........).

WHAT TO DO IF YOU HAVE A COMPLAINT

If you have a complaint about this home condition report or the home inspector who carried it out, you should follow the procedures set out below.

- Ask the company who provided the report, (the company named on the front of the report) or the home inspector who carried it out to give you a copy of their complaints handling procedure. All companies must have a written procedure and make it available to you if you ask.
- Follow the guidance given in the document, which includes making a formal complaint.
- Companies that provide home condition reports must handle your complaint in accordance with their procedure.

You may ask (scheme name) to investigate the complaint if:

- your complaint is about an allegation of criminal activity;
- the company fails to handle your complaint in line with their procedure; or
- you are not happy with how they have handled your complaint.

You can write to them at (address).

(The Certification Scheme's procedures for dealing with consumer complaints will be outlined here when they are finalised.)

WHAT TO DO IF YOU ARE THE SELLER AND BELIEVE THAT THE REPORT IS INCORRECT

If you believe that the report is incorrect, you should report this to the company that provided the report (or the home inspector who carried out the inspection).

If the company or the inspector agrees that details are not correct, they will give a corrected report and ask for the inaccurate report to be removed from the register of home condition reports.

If the company or inspector do not agree, you may complain to (scheme name) and apply to have the report removed from the register of home condition reports.

6 Example HCRs: 1930s and listed properties

This chapter contains two further example properties, each presented with a series of photographs and a completed Home Condition Report. Along with the previous case study, these HCRs help to illustrate how reporting styles need to be adapted to reflect different individual property types. **The properties contain some obvious defects and deficiencies, and closer photographs help to show their form and construction.**

EXAMPLE ONE: 1930s PROPERTY

This example includes a semi-detached house that was built around the 1930s and is located in an inter-war suburb of Piketown-on-Sea. The inspection of this property took approximately 150 minutes – around the same amount of time needed to carry out an equivalent HSV inspection.

View of garage roof from landing window

Front elevation

Rear elevation

Main roof viewed from rear garden

Side wall adjacent to open gulley

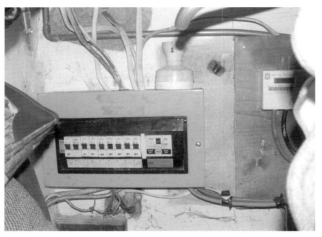

Electrical switchgear in under stair cupboard

EXAMPLE TWO: GRADE II LISTED PROPERTY

This example includes a seventeenth century Grade II listed building that is located within a small rural hamlet known as The Swim (around four miles from Piketown-on-Sea). The inspection of this property took approximately 240 minutes. Given this property's age and listed status, most surveyors would prefer to carry out a full building survey, but an equivalent HSV would have typically taken around 240 minutes to complete.

Front elevation

Rear elevation

Lower left hand section viewed from front garden

Eaves detail, front elevation

Front dormer window from rear sloping area

1930s PROPERTY HOME CONDITION REPORT

INTRODUCTION AND TERMS REGARDING THE ROLE OF THE HOME INSPECTOR WOULD NORMALLY APPEAR HERE. REFER BACK TO PAGE 49 FOR FURTHER INFORMATION.

SECTION A

GENERAL INFORMATION

HOME CONDITION REPORT

Address of the property that has been inspected:	13 Suburban Avenue Piketown-on-Sea Pikeshire, MM1 1MN
Property reference number (if known):	987656
Home inspector's name:	JR Hartley
Home inspector's licence number:	012345
Company name:	Home Inspectors.co.uk Ltd
Company address and postcode:	1 High Street Tenchtown Pikeshire, MM1 2SS
Company email address:	JRH@homeinspectors.co.uk
Company telephone number:	002020202020202
Company fax number:	002020202020201
Date of the inspection	5th December 2005
Report Reference Number:	9098765434
The Report Reference Number(s) of Home condition reports written for this property in the last 12 months:	Not applicable
Disclosure on Related Parties*	Not applicable

NOTE: Statements e.g. 'Date of the inspection' will appear on the public version. However, questions, (identified in brackets) are prompts for completion of the form but will not appear on the public version.

SECTION B

SUMMARY

Date of the inspection:	5th December 2005
Full address and postcode of the property:	13 Suburban Avenue Piketown-on-Sea Pikeshire, MM1 1MN
Weather conditions:	The weather at the time of inspection was dry.
The state of property when inspected. (Was the property furnished or unfurnished?)	The property was occupied and furnished.
Approximate year of construction (When was the property built?)	1930
Approximate year when the property was extended. (When was the extension built?)	The rear extension and attached garage were built in 1980. The front porch was built in 1985. The attached conservatory was built in 1995.
When was the property converted?	
Type of property:	The property is a semi-detached house.
Are there any signs of tenants living in the property?	
Is the property in an area occupied primarily by tenants?	No

Accommodation

Storey	Living Rooms	Bed-rooms	Bath and/ or shower	Separate WC	Kitchen	Utility Room	Conservatory (hot or cold)	Other	Name of 'Other'
Lower Ground									
Ground	2			1	1		1		
First		4	1						
Second									
Third									
Fourth									
Roof space									
Totals	2	4	1	1	1	0	1	0	0

House only: Gross external floor area (m²) | 130 | Reinstatement Cost | £143,000

Flat only: Gross internal floor area (m²) | –

Note: This reinstatement cost is the estimated cost of completely rebuilding the property. It represents the sum at which the home should be insured against fire and other risks. It is based on building and other related costs and does not include the value of the land the home is built on. It does not include leisure facilities such as swimming pools and tennis courts. The figure should be reviewed regularly as building costs change. Importantly, it is not a valuation of the property.

If the property is very large or historic, or if it incorporates special features or is of unusual construction and a specialist would be needed to assess the reinstatement cost, no cost figure is provided and the report says that a specialist is needed.

Construction

| A short general description of the construction | The roofs to the property are covered by tile and the walls are of brick and tile. The floors are of mixed timber and solid construction, and the windows are of mixed timber and plastic. |

Mains Services

The ticked boxes indicate that mains services are connected

Drainage	Gas	Electricity	Water
✓	✓	✓	✓

Central Heating

| The property does not have central heating. |

Outside Facilities

(Is a garage provided?)	There is a single attached garage.
(Is the garage on or off the site?)	The garage is on site.
(Is the garage part of the building?)	Yes
(Is the garage a single, double or more?)	Single
(Is there a carport?)	No
(Number of allocated parking spaces?)	One
(Are these on or off the site?)	On-site
(Are there any gardens which are part of the property?)	Yes
(Are the gardens to the front, side or back?)	There are gardens to the front and rear of the property.
(Are there any outbuildings with the property?)	There are no permanent outbuildings.
(Are the roads and footpaths made up?)	Yes

Summary of Ratings

(This is generated by the system from the information the inspector provides.)

Section of the Report	Part Number	Part Name	Identifier (if there is more than one entry in the table)	Rating
D: Outside condition	D1	Chimney stacks	A) Left hand chimney stack B) Rear chimney stack	A) 2 B) 2
	D2	Roof coverings	C) Main pitched roof D) Flat roof	C) 2 D) 1
	D3	Rain water pipes & gutters	X	1
	D4	Main walls and claddings	A) Original building B) Rear extension C) Front porch	A) 2 B) 1 C) 1
	D5	Windows	X	2
	D6	External doors	X	1
	D7	All other woodwork	X	1
	D8	Outside decoration	X	1
	D9	Other outside detail	X	–
E: Inside condition	E1	Roof structure	X	2
	E2	Ceilings	X	1
	E3	Internal walls, partitions & plasterwork	X	1
	E4	Floors	X	1
	E5	Fireplaces & chimney breasts (and the outside of flues)	A) Front reception B) Rear reception C) Front bedroom D) Centre bedroom E) Rear bedroom	A) 1 B) 1 C) 2 D) 2 E) 2
	E6	Built-in fittings	X	1
	E7	Inside woodwork (staircase, joinery, etc.)	X	2
	E8	Bathroom fittings	X	1
	E9	Dampness	X	1
	E10	Other issues	X	–
F: Services	F1	Electricity	X	3
	F2	Gas/Oil	X	1
	F3	Water	X	1
	F4	Heating	X	1
	F5	Drainage	X	1

Overall condition of the property

> The property is in a fair condition, but some works of repair and maintenance are required.

Summary of structural movement

> There is no evidence of serious structural movement.

Further Investigation

Recommended investigation of defects seen or suspected:

> Your attention is drawn to the following matters for which further investigation is recommended by someone who is appropriately qualified:
>
> - Electrical Installation (Section F1)
> - Asbestos (Section G)

SECTION C

CONVEYANCING AND HEALTH & SAFETY ISSUES

ISSUES FOR CONVEYANCERS

The home inspector does not act as 'the conveyancer'. However, if during the inspection, the inspector identifies issues that the conveyancers advising the buyer and seller may need to investigate further, the inspector will refer to these in the report. This is to draw the issues to the attention of others to improve the quality of the information in the home information pack. The inspector will not have seen the legal and other documents in the home information pack.

The conveyancer should investigate the issues below:

Drainage	The property has a shared drainage system situated outside the boundaries.
Planning and any other permission needed	The property has been altered by the construction of a rear extension, a front porch and garage, which may have required statutory consents.
Previous structural repairs New building warranties Building insurance (ongoing claims)	I understand that certain works including installation of double glazing and a conservatory have been carried out to the property under warranty or guarantee.

DANGEROUS MATERIALS AND CONTAMINATED LAND, SUBSIDENCE AND FLOODING

The home inspector assumes that:

- The home is not built with nor contains hazardous materials; and it is not built on contaminated land. However, if any of these materials are found during the inspection, or if the home inspector finds evidence to suspect that the land may be contaminated, this will be shown on the report along with recommendations for further investigations.

HEALTH AND SAFETY RISKS

The home inspector will draw your attention to items from a set list of health and safety issues if they are seen at the property.

The inspector does not have to identify risks which have existed in the property for a long time, and which cannot reasonably be changed. As an example, the inspector will not draw your attention to uneven floor surfaces that have existed for decades.

- The risk of injury is increased by the lack of safety glass in the lounge and dining room doors.
- No evidence is available to confirm the recent testing of the gas appliances. Failure to test and service increases safety risks.
- No evidence is available to confirm the recent testing of the electrical installation. Failure to test and service increases safety risks.

SECTION D

OUTSIDE CONDITION

The inspector carried out a non-invasive inspection of the outside of the main building and permanent outbuildings. They made this inspection from various points within the boundaries of the property and from public areas such as footpaths and open spaces, using binoculars where necessary. The inspector did not stand on walls or enter neighbouring private property. They examined roofs, chimneys and other external surfaces of the building from the ground. They inspected flat roofs to single-storey buildings from a ladder, where the surface of the roof was not more than three-metres above ground level. They did not inspect features above this level that cannot be seen from any point. Because of the risk of causing damage, the inspector did not walk on flat roofs. They assessed rainwater fittings (gutters and downpipes) only if there was heavy rain at the time of inspection.

The inspector looked at the overall condition and the state of repair of the outside parts of the property. The report does not reflect every minor blemish and does not point out each individual minor defect in the outside walls. However, where there are so many minor defects that together they are serious, the report will say this.

FLATS: OUTSIDE INSPECTION

When inspecting blocks of flats, it is often difficult to see the whole outside of a building or block, and its maintenance is rarely the responsibility of one person. The inspector only carried out a non-invasive inspection to the level of detail set out above, to the main walls, windows and roof over the flat.

The inspector did not inspect the rest of the block to this level of detail; but instead has formed an opinion based on a general inspection of the rest of the block. They provide information about the outside and shared parts so that the conveyancer can check whether the maintenance clauses in the lease or other title documents are adequate.

The inspector inspected the shared access to the flat together with the area where car parking and any garage for the flat are, along with the access to that area. They did not inspect other shared parts, such as separate halls, stairs and access ways to other flats in the block, the lift motor room and cleaning cupboards.

I could not inspect the inner surfaces of the rear chimney stack because they could not be viewed from within the property boundaries or adjoining public areas.

D1 CHIMNEY STACKS	
Identifying name for the part (where more than one is recorded.)	A) Left hand chimney stack B) Rear chimney stack
Condition Rating	A) Left hand chimney stack – 2 B) Rear chimney stack – 2
Justification for Rating and Comments	The chimney stacks are of brick. The brickwork to the stacks is eroded and stained. This requires repair or replacement, but is not considered serious or urgent.

SECTION D (continued)

D2 ROOF COVERINGS	
Identifying name for the part (where more than one is recorded.)	A) Main pitched roof B) Flat roof
Condition Rating	A) Main pitched roof – 2 B) Flat roof – 1
Justification for Rating and Comments	The main and porch roofs are sloping and covered with plain concrete tiles. The tiles, in particular to the rear roof slopes are slipped and some are missing. The mortar beddings to the ridge and hip tiles have eroded. The sloping roof coverings are moss covered in places. This requires repair or replacement, but is not considered serious or urgent. The rear extension roof is flat and covered with mineral felt or similar material. No repair is presently required.

D3 RAIN WATER PIPES & GUTTERS	
Identifying name for the part (where more than one is recorded.)	
Condition Rating	1
Justification for Rating and Comments	The rainwater fittings are of plastic. These have been renewed in recent years. The gutters, in particular to the rear of the house have become blocked with moss. The side gulley adjacent to the kitchen is also blocked with debris. No repair is presently required. Normal maintenance must be undertaken.

D4 MAIN WALLS & CLADDINGS	
Identifying name for the part (where more than one is recorded.)	A) Original building B) Rear extension C) Front porch
Condition Rating	A) Original building – 2 B) Rear extension – 1 C) Front porch – 1
Justification for Rating and Comments	The walls to the original building and the rear extension are 275mm thick and are of cavity construction, mainly brick, with rendered and tiled facings. The brickwork is generally stained and the pointing, in particular to the lower right hand wall has eroded. The damp proof course, in particular to the front wall of the main building is bridged. This requires repair or replacement, but is not considered serious or urgent. The walls to the front porch are 125mm single skin brick construction. No repair is presently required.

SECTION D (continued)

D5 WINDOWS	
Identifying name for the part (where more than one is recorded.)	–
Condition Rating	2
Justification for Rating and Comments	The window frames are a mixture of timber and plastic. Some are double glazed. The timber window frames, in particular to the kitchen are draughty and rotten. The sealed double glazing units, in particular to the front living room windows are misted. This requires repair or replacement, but is not considered serious or urgent.

D6 EXTERNAL DOORS	
Identifying name for the part (where more than one is recorded.)	–
Condition Rating	1
Justification for Rating and Comments	The external doors are a mixture of glazed timber and plastic. No repair is presently required.

D7 ALL OTHER WOODWORK	
Identifying name for the part (where more than one is recorded.)	–
Condition Rating	1
Justification for Rating and Comments	The external woodwork has been replaced in recent years with plastic. No repair is presently required.

D8 OUTSIDE DECORATION	
Identifying name for the part (where more than one is recorded.)	–
Condition Rating	1
Justification for Rating and Comments	Decorated areas include the exterior doors and some windows. The decorations, in particular to the window are faded and peeling. No repair is presently required, but normal maintenance must be undertaken.

D9 OTHER OUTSIDE DETAIL	
Identifying name for the part (where more than one is recorded.)	There are no other external details.
Condition Rating	–
Justification for Rating and Comments	–

SECTION E

INSIDE CONDITION

The home inspector carried out a non-invasive inspection of all the parts of the home they could see without causing damage. However, if the inspector could not see a part of the home without the risk of damage, and they suspect that there could be a problem, the report will say this and include recommendations on the need for further investigation.

The home inspector checked for damp in vulnerable areas by using a moisture-measuring meter.

They inspected the roof structure from inside the roof space where it was accessible but did not move or lift insulation material, stored goods and other contents. The inspector did not walk around the space if there was a risk to safety (for example, where insulation covers the ceiling joists); instead they inspected the roof from the access point.

They opened some of the windows and all the doors, they inspected floor surfaces and under-floor spaces where they were readily accessible, they did not move or lift furniture, floor coverings or other contents. The home inspector has not commented on sound insulation or chimney flues (or both), because it is rarely practical to do so without using specialist equipment that home inspectors do not carry.

I could not fully inspect the understair cupboard because the area was filled with stored items.

E1 ROOF STRUCTURE	
Identifying name for the part (where more than one is recorded.)	–
Condition Rating	2
Justification for Rating and Comments	The main roof frame is constructed of cut softwood timber. The roof timbers are infested by wood boring beetle. This requires repair or replacement, but is not considered serious or urgent.

E2 CEILINGS	
Identifying name for the part (where more than one is recorded.)	–
Condition Rating	1
Justification for Rating and Comments	The ceilings are a mixture of lath and plaster and plasterboard. The lath and plaster ceilings are uneven and affected by cracking. The ceiling in the right hand front bedroom is covered by polystyrene tiles which may be a hazard in the event of a fire. No repair is presently required, but normal maintenance must be undertaken.

SECTION E (continued)

E3 INTERNAL WALLS, PARTITIONS & PLASTERWORK	
Identifying name for the part (where more than one is recorded.)	–
Condition Rating	1
Justification for Rating and Comments	The internal walls and partitions are a mixture of solid and lightweight timber construction. Internal finishes, in particular to the kitchen are uneven and incomplete. No repair is presently required, but normal maintenance must be undertaken.

E4 FLOORS	
Identifying name for the part (where more than one is recorded.)	–
Condition Rating	1
Justification for Rating and Comments	The floors are a mixture of suspended timber and solid construction. The floors, in particular to the front and rear reception rooms are poorly ventilated. No repair is presently required, but normal maintenance must be undertaken.

E5 FIREPLACES & CHIMNEY BREASTS (AND THE OUTSIDE OF FLUES)	
Identifying name for the part (where more than one is recorded.)	A) Front reception B) Rear reception C) Front bedroom D) Centre bedroom E) Rear bedroom
Condition Rating	A) Front reception – 1 B) Rear reception – 1 C) Front bedroom – 2 D) Centre bedroom – 2 E) Rear bedroom – 2
Justification for Rating and Comments	The chimney breasts are of mainly brick construction with a plaster finish. Some of the fireplace openings contain gas fires. The chimney breasts to the front, centre and rear bedrooms are inadequately ventilated. This requires repair or replacement, but is not considered serious or urgent.

SECTION E (continued)

E6 BUILT-IN FITTINGS	
Identifying name for the part (where more than one is recorded.)	–
Condition Rating	1
Justification for Rating and Comments	The built-in fittings including kitchen fitments and wardrobes are a mixture of softwood and medium density fibreboard (commonly known as MDF). The kitchen fitments are dated and there is damage, in particular around the sink. No repair is presently required, but normal maintenance must be undertaken.

E7 INSIDE WOODWORK (STAIRCASE, JOINERY, ETC.)	
Identifying name for the part (where more than one is recorded.)	–
Condition Rating	2
Justification for Rating and Comments	The internal woodwork (including doors, skirtings, bannisters and staircases) is of mainly sofwood construction. The kitchen door is missing and may provide inadequate protection in the event of fire. Doors, in particular to the front living room and dining room have no safety glass. This requires repair or replacement, but is not considered serious or urgent.

E8 BATHROOM FITTINGS	
Identifying name for the part (where more than one is recorded.)	–
Condition Rating	1
Justification for Rating and Comments	The sanitary fittings in the bathroom comprise a pressed steel panelled bath, low level ceramic WC and ceramic wash hand basin. The fittings are worn and dated. No repair is presently required, but normal maintenance must be undertaken.

SECTION E (continued)

E9 DAMPNESS	
Identifying name for the part (where more than one is recorded.)	–
Condition Rating	1
Justification for Rating and Comments	There is evidence of a bituminous felt damp proof course to the main building and polythene damp proof courses to the rear extension and porch. Condensation is affecting the walls of the front bedroom, likely to have been caused by an imbalance of heating and ventilation. This may affect other parts of the property. No repair is presently required, but normal maintenance must be undertaken.

E10 OTHER ISSUES	
Identifying name for the part (where more than one is recorded.)	There are no other internal issues.
Condition Rating	–
Justification for Rating and Comments	–

SECTION F

SERVICES

Services are generally hidden within the construction of the property; for example, pipes are beneath the floors and wiring is within the walls. As a result only the visible parts of the available services can be inspected. Specialist tests were not carried out. The visual inspection does not assess the services to make sure they work properly and efficiently and meet modern standards. If any services (such as the boiler or mains water) are turned off, the home inspector will state that in the report and will not turn them on.

Otherwise, the home inspector turned on some taps on appliances and, where safe and practical to do so, lifted the covers on the drainage inspection chambers. The home inspector reports only on the services covered in this section (electricity, gas, oil, water, heating and drainage). All other services and domestic appliances are not included in the reporting: for example, security and door-answering systems, smoke alarms, television, cable, wireless and satellite communication systems, cookers, hobs, washing machines and fridges (even where built-in). The report gives some general advice on safety and the importance of maintaining the services in the home.

F1 ELECTRICITY	
General Advice endorsed by the Institute of Electrical Engineers	*Safety Warning: Periodic inspection and testing of electrical installations is important to protect your home from damage and to ensure the safety of the occupants. Guidance published by the Institute of Electrical Engineers recommends that inspections and testing are undertaken at least every 10 years and on change of occupancy.* *All electrical installation work undertaken after 1st January 2005 should be identified by an Electrical Installation Certificate.*
Condition Rating	3
Justification for Rating and Comments	There is a mains electricity supply and the meter is located in the understairs cupboard. The installation is of a poor quality. The cables, in particular to the understairs cupboard are poorly clipped. The sockets in a number of rooms are old. Further advice should be obtained.

F2 GAS/OIL	
General Advice endorsed by CORGI (Council of Registered Gas Installers)	*Safety Warning: Regular servicing of the gas installation and all gas appliances is important to ensure you protect your home from damage and to ensure the safety of the occupants. This MUST be carried out by a CORGI registered installer. If there is no current certificate relating to an appliance installation, a CORGI registered installer should check and test the installation.*
General Advice endorsed by OFTEC (Oil Firing Technical Association)	*Safety Warning: Periodic inspection and testing of equipment connected with oil installations is important to protect your home and environment and to reduce risks from fire, carbon monoxide poisoning and pollution from leaks. Full advice can be obtained from OFTEC.*
Condition Rating	1
Justification for Rating and Comments	There is a mains gas supply and the meter is in the understairs cupboard. No repair is presently required, but normal maintenance must be undertaken.

SECTION F (continued)

F3 WATER	
Condition Rating	1
Justification for Rating and Comments	The water pipe work is copper and the stopcock is in the understairs cupboard. No repair is presently required, but normal maintenance must be undertaken.

F4 HEATING	
Condition Rating	1
Justification for Rating and Comments	There is no central heating. Space heating is provided by gas fires. Hot water is provided by wall-hung gas multipoint. No repair is presently required, but normal maintenance must be undertaken.

F5 DRAINAGE	
Condition Rating	1
Justification for Rating and Comments	There is a mains drainage system. Surface water is combined with the foul drainage system. No repair is presently required, but normal maintenance must be undertaken.

SECTION G

GROUNDS

The home inspector inspected the condition of the boundary walls, outbuildings and shared facilities.

To inspect these areas the home inspector walked around the grounds. The report provides a summary of the general condition of any garden walls, fences, and permanent outbuildings. Conservatories with translucent or clear roofs attached to the main buildings are treated as outbuildings, as are garages and permanent store sheds. Buildings containing swimming pools and sports facilities are also treated as outbuildings, but the home inspector does not report on the leisure facilities, such as the pool itself and its equipment.

The inspector did not inspect leisure facilities, landscaping and other facilities, including swimming pools and tennis courts, and non-permanent outbuildings.

I could not inspect the surface of the garage roof due to piled up sheet materials, or the interior of the garage due to the area being filled with stored items.

The garage is of sectional pre-cast reinforced concrete construction under a steel-framed roof with corrugated cement fibre roof sheeting. The garage is in a poor condition and some works of repair and maintenance are required, particularly to the damaged and leaking roof. The sheet roofing may contain asbestos and a further inspection is recommended.

The boundary walls are of brick construction. The right hand front boundary wall leans heavily and there is damage to the front boundary wall. This requires repair or replacement, but is not considered serious or urgent.

Pavings are uneven and breaking up in places.

SECTION H

ENERGY PERFORMANCE CERTIFICATE

Section H: Energy Performance Certificate
Save money, improve comfort and help the environment

The following report is based on an inspection carried out for:

Address:
13, Suburban Avenue,
Piketown-on-sea,
Pikeshire, MM1 1MN

Building type:	Home
Whole or part:	Whole
Methodology:	RDSAP
Inspection date:	5/12/2005

Certif. Number:	
Date issued:	
Inspector name:	

This home's performance ratings

This home has been inspected and its performance rated in terms of its energy efficiency and environmental impact. This is calculated using the UK Standard Assessment Procedure (SAP) for dwellings which gives you an energy efficiency rating based on fuel cost and an environmental impact rating based on carbon dioxide (CO_2) emissions.

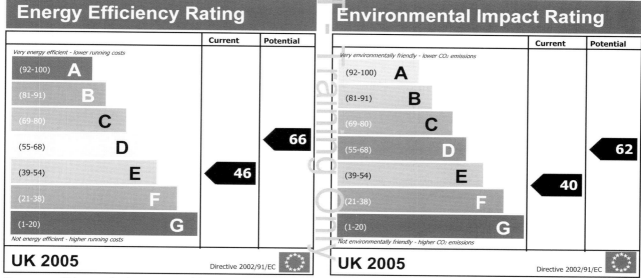

The energy efficiency rating is a measure of the overall efficiency of a home. The higher the rating the more energy efficient the home is and the lower the fuel bills will be.

The environmental impact rating is a measure of this home's impact on the environment. The higher the rating the less impact it has on the environment.

Typical fuel costs and carbon dioxide (CO_2) emissions of this home

This table provides you with an indication of how much it will cost to provide lighting, heating and hot water to this home. The fuel costs and carbon dioxide emissions are calculated based on a SAP assessment of the actual energy use that would be needed to deliver the defined level of comfort in this home, using standard occupancy assumptions, which are described on page 4. The energy use includes the energy used in producing and delivering the fuels to this home. The fuel costs only take into account the cost of fuel and not any associated service, maintenance or safety inspection costs. The costs have been provided for guidance only as it is unlikely they will match actual costs for any particular household.

	Current	Potential
Energy use	46,279 kWh/m2 per year	26,908 kWh/m2 per year
Carbon dioxide emissions	9.3 tonnes per year	5.5 tonnes per year
Lighting	£94 per year	£82 per year
Heating	£639 per year	£353 per year
Hot water	£94 per year	£63 per year

To see how this home's performance ratings can be improved please go to page 2

Section H: Energy Performance Certificate

Summary of this home's energy performance related features

The table shows the current performance of each element of this home on the following scale:
Extremely poor/ Very poor/ Poor/ Average/ Good/ Very good/ Excellent

Element	Description	Current performance
Main walls	CA Cavity:, Insulation: A As Built, Cavity U: 1.60	???
Main roof	P Pitched, Insulation at: J Joists, Thickness: 50 mm	???
Main floor	U: 0.60 A: 69.09 m2	???
Windows	N Normal, Doble Glazed: 60%, Double-glazing Installed: Pre	???
Main heating	JAA	???
Main heating controls	CRB Appliance stat	???
Secondary heating	JAA Efficiency: 50.00%	???
Hot water	HGM Multi-point gas water heater	???
Lighting	Rooms: 9, L.E.L. Fittings: 0, External lights: None	???
Current energy efficiency rating		**E 46**
Current environmental impact rating		**E 40**

Measures to improve this home's performance ratings

The improved energy ratings are cumulative, that is they assume the improvements have been installed in the order that they appear in the table.

Lower cost measures	Typical savings	Energy rating after improvement
Draughtproof all doors and windows	£10	E 47
Install cavity wall insulation	£127	D 55
Sub Total	£137	
Higher cost measures		
Install fully controlled gas condensing boiler and radiators for heating and hot water	£151	D 65
Sub Total	£151	
Potential energy efficiency rating		**D 66**
Potential environmental impact rating		**D 62**

Further measures to achieve even higher standards

Double glaze the single glazed windows	£10	D 65
Install solar panel (3 m2)	£25	D 66
Enhanced energy efficiency rating		**D 66**
Enhanced environmental impact rating		**D 65**

Improvements to the energy efficiency and environmental impact ratings will usually be in step with each other. However, they can sometimes diverge because reduced energy costs are very occasionally not accompanied by reduced carbon dioxide emissions.

Section H: Energy Performance Certificate

Measures to reduce the running costs and improve this home's energy ratings

Lower cost measures (typically up to £500 each)

These improvements are relatively cheap to install and will be worth tackling first.

Measure 1

Cavity wall

The external walls of your home are built with a gap, called a cavity, between the inside and outside layers of the wall. Cavity wall insulation fills this gap with an insulating material. The material is pumped into the gap through small holes, which are drilled into the outside layer of the walls (the small holes are sealed up afterwards). Because this involves using specialist machinery, a professional installation company must carry out the work. The contractor will thoroughly survey your walls before commencing work to be sure that this type of insulation is right for your home, and provide a guarantee for the work.

Measure 2

Topping up loft insulation

The anticipated cost is based upon a contractor installing an additional 100mm of glass fibre or mineral wool insulation in your loft, but it can also be installed by a capable DIY enthusiast. If you choose a DIY installation then take care not to block ventilation at the edge of the loft space as this may cause condensation. When handling the insulation always wear gloves and a mask.

Measure 3

Hot water and pipe insulation

Improving the insulation of your hot water tank using a very thick jacket will help reduce your heating bills. You should also insulate the hot water pipe connections to the cylinder, for about a metre, or as far as you can get access to them. Fit the jacket over the top of any existing jacket and over any thermostat clamped to the cylinder.

Higher cost measures (typically up to £3000 each)

Measure 4

Condensing boiler

This improvement is most appropriate when your existing central heating boiler needs repair or replacement. A condensing boiler is capable of much higher efficiencies than other types of boiler, meaning it will burn less fuel to heat your property. Only a qualified heating engineer should carry out the installation. [Building Regulations apply to this work, so you should get advice from your local Building Control Authority].

Measure 5

Installation of full controls package

Although your heating sytem already has a room thermostat, you can save more money by adding thermostatic radiator valves as well. They allow you to control the temperature of each room to suit your needs, adding to comfort and reducing your bills. For example, you can set them to be warmer in your living room and bathroom than in your bedrooms. You will need a plumber to fit them to every radiator except one - the radiator in the same room as your room thermostat. You still need the room thermostat, because without it, even when the TRVs have turned off the radiators, the boiler is still burning fuel and wasting your money - so don't let the plumber remove it.

Further measures to achieve an even higher standard

These measures should be considered if aiming for the highest possible standard for this home.

Measure 6

Double glazing

Replacing the existing single glazed windows with double-glazing will improve your comfort in your home by reducing draughts and cold spots near windows. This will also help to save on your heating bills during the long winter months. Building Regulations apply to this work, so you should either use a contractor who is registered with Fensa or get advice from your local Building Control Authority.

Measure 7

Solar water heating

Energy from the sun can be harnessed to provide domestic hot water. These systems do not generally provide space heating, and are described as 'Solar Thermal' systems. They are among the most cost effective renewable energy systems that can be installed on dwellings in urban or rural environments.

Section H: Energy Performance Certificate

About this energy inspection

Energy inspections are not new. They have been available in the UK since the late 1980's. Your inspection has been undertaken by a qualified inspector who has been trained to collect the correct information about the energy efficiency of your home. This information has been processed by a Government approved organisation to produce the energy rating and suggestions in the report. Both the inspector and the energy report supplier are regularly monitored to show that their work is up to standard.

If you would like clarification of the technical information in this energy report please contact the:

Inspector Stuart Fairlie on 01788 833 386

Inspector Registration Number   1000-0009

About this home's performance ratings

The ratings provide you with a measure of the overall energy efficiency of this home and its environmental impact. Both are calculated using the Standard Assessment Procedure (SAP), which is the Government's recommended system of assessing the energy efficiency of dwellings. The ratings take into account the home's insulation, heating systems, hot water system, fixed lighting, ventilation, number of windows and related fuels.

Not all of us use our homes in the same way so to allow one home to be directly compared to another, energy ratings are calculated using 'standard occupancy' assumptions. Standard occupancy assumes that the house is heated for 9 hours a day during weekdays and 16 hours a day at weekends, with the living room heated to 21°C and the rest of the house at 18°C.

The ratings are expressed on a scale of 1 to 100. The higher the energy efficiency rating the more energy efficient the home and the higher the environmental impact rating the less impact it has on the environment.

Homes which are more energy efficient use less energy, saving money and helping to protect the environment. A home with an energy efficiency rating of 100 would be energy self sufficient and so the cost of providing lighting, heating and hot water would be practically zero.

The potential rating shown on page one is the economic potential of the home assuming all cost effective measures have been installed. A home built to the 2005 Building Regulations would typically be at the boundary of bands B and C.

This home's impact on the environment

Carbon dioxide is one of the biggest contributors to the man-made greenhouse effect. The energy we use to heat, light and power our homes produces 28 per cent of the UK's CO_2 emissions.

The average household in the UK creates about six tonnes of CO_2 every year. There are simple steps you can take to cut CO_2 emissions and help prevent climate change. Making your home more energy efficient by adopting the suggestions in this report can help protect the environment by saving CO_2. You could save even more CO_2 by switching to renewable energy sources.

What can I do today?

In addition to the specific measures suggested in this report, don't forget there are many simple measures you can put into action today that will save you money and help reduce your impact on the environment.

For example:

- Check that your heating system thermostat is not set too high (21°C in the living room is suggested)
- Make sure your hot water is not too hot (60°C is suggested)
- Turn off your lights and domestic appliances when not needed, and do not leave TVs and videos on standby
- Do not overfill kettles and saucepans, and use a lid where possible
- Buy energy saving recommended appliances
- Find out if you are eligible for grants or offers to help with the cost of energy saving measures by visiting **www.est.org.uk/myhome** or calling **0800 512 012**.

GRADE II LISTED PROPERTY HOME CONDITION REPORT

INTRODUCTION AND TERMS REGARDING THE ROLE OF THE HOME INSPECTOR WOULD NORMALLY APPEAR HERE. REFER BACK TO PAGE 49 FOR FURTHER INFORMATION.

SECTION A

GENERAL INFORMATION

HOME CONDITION REPORT

Address of the property that has been inspected:	Period Cottage The Swim Pikeshire, MM1 1MN
Property reference number (if known):	987657
Home inspector's name:	JR Hartley
Home inspector's licence number:	012345
Company name:	Home Inspectors.co.uk Ltd
Company address and postcode:	1 High Street Tenchtown Pikeshire, MM1 2SS
Company email address:	JRH@homeinspectors.co.uk
Company telephone number:	002020202020202
Company fax number:	002020202020201
Date of the inspection:	6th December 2005
Report Reference Number:	9098765435
The Report Reference Number(s) of Home condition reports written for this property in the last 12 months:	0
Disclosure on Related Parties*	Not applicable

NOTE: Statements e.g. 'Date of the inspection' will appear on the public version. However, questions, (identified in brackets) are prompts for completion of the form but will not appear on the public version.

SECTION B

SUMMARY

Date of the inspection:	6th December 2005
Full address and postcode of the property:	Period Cottage, The Swim, Pikeshire, MM1 1MN
Weather conditions:	The weather at the time of inspection was dry.
The state of property when inspected. (Was the property furnished or unfurnished?)	The property was occupied and furnished.
Approximate year of construction (When was the property built?)	1650
Approximate year when the property was extended. (When was the extension built?)	The side extension was built in 1950.
When was the property converted?	
Type of property:	The property is a detached house.
Are there any signs of tenants living in the property?	
Is the property in an area occupied primarily by tenants?	No
Is the property in a conservation area or likely to be listed?	The property is listed and situated in a conservation area.
Listing grade (if known):	Grade II

Accommodation

Storey	Living Rooms	Bed-rooms	Bath and/ or shower	Separate WC	Kitchen	Utility Room	Conservatory (hot or cold)	Other	Name of 'Other'
Lower Ground									
Ground	2		1	1	1				
First		3	1						
Second									
Third									
Fourth									
Roof space									
Totals	2	3	2	1	1	0	0	0	

House only: Gross external floor area (m²)	250	Reinstatement Cost	In view of the historic nature of the property, specialist advice is required to assess its reinstatement cost for insurance purposes.
Flat only: Gross internal floor area (m²)	–		

Note: This reinstatement cost is the estimated cost of completely rebuilding the property. It represents the sum at which the home should be insured against fire and other risks. It is based on building and other related costs and does not include the value of the land the home is built on. It does not include leisure facilities such as swimming pools and tennis courts. The figure should be reviewed regularly as building costs change. Importantly, it is not a valuation of the property.

If the property is very large or historic, or if it incorporates special features or is of unusual construction and a specialist would be needed to assess the reinstatement cost, no cost figure is provided and the report says that a specialist is needed.

Construction

A short general description

> The roofs to the property are covered by tile with felted flat dormers, and the walls are of brick.
> The floors are of mixed timber and solid construction, and the windows are of timber casement style.

Mains Services

The ticked boxes indicate that mains services are connected

Drainage	Gas	Electricity	Water
✓	✓	✓	✓

> There is a private drainage system.
> There is a private oil supply.

Central Heating

> The property has a partial, oil fired central heating system.

Outside Facilities

(Is a garage provided?)	Yes
(Is the garage on or off the site?)	On site
(Is the garage a single, double or more?)	Double
(Are there any gardens which are part of the property?)	Yes
(Are the gardens to the front, side or back?)	There are gardens to the front, side and rear of the property.
(Are there any outbuildings with the property?)	There are no permanent outbuildings.
(Are the roads and footpaths made up?)	Yes

Summary of Ratings

(This is generated by the system from the information the inspector provides.)

Section of the Report	Part Number	Part Name	Identifier (if there is more than one entry in the table)	Rating
D: Outside condition	D1	Chimney stacks	A) Front chimney stack B) Rear chimney stack	A) 2 B) 1
	D2	Roof coverings	A) Sloping roofs B) Flat dormer roofs	A) 2 B) 2
	D3	Rain water pipes & gutters	X	2
	D4	Main walls and claddings	A) Original building B) Side extension C) Damp proof course	A) 2 B) 1 C) 1
	D5	Windows	X	2
	D6	External doors	X	2
	D7	All other woodwork	X	2
	D8	Outside decoration	X	2
	D9	Other outside detail	X	–
E: Inside condition	E1	Roof structure	A) Roof structure B) Roof space	A) 2 B) 2
	E2	Ceilings	X	2
	E3	Internal walls, partitions & plasterwork	X	2
	E4	Floors	X	2
	E5	Fireplaces & chimney breasts (and the outside of flues)	X	2
	E6	Built-in fittings	X	1
	E7	Inside woodwork (staircase, joinery, etc.)	X	2
	E8	Bathroom fittings	X	1
	E9	Dampness	X	1
	E10	Other issues	X	–
F: Services	F1	Electricity	X	1
	F2	Gas/Oil	X	1
	F3	Water	X	1
	F4	Heating	X	1
	F5	Drainage	X	1

Overall condition of the property	The property is in a fair condition, but some works of repair and maintenance are required.
Widespread problems that affect many parts of the property.	There are defects including wood beetle infestation affecting multiple parts of the property.
Summary of structural movement	There is movement cracking, structural tie straps and bulging to the outer walls, particularly the front wall, but I saw no evidence to suggest this is ongoing. There are a number of trees growing within the site which are likely to represent a risk to the structural integrity of the property. Further investigation is recommended.

Further Investigation

Recommended investigation of defects seen or suspected:	Your attention is drawn to the following matter for which further investigation is recommended by someone who is appropriately qualified: • Dampness and timber defects (Section D7) • Trees (Section B)

SECTION C

CONVEYANCING AND HEALTH & SAFETY ISSUES

ISSUES FOR CONVEYANCERS

The home inspector does not act as 'the conveyancer'. However, if during the inspection, the inspector identifies issues that the conveyancers advising the buyer and seller may need to investigate further, the inspector will refer to these in the report. This is to draw the issues to the attention of others to improve the quality of the information in the home information pack. The inspector will not have seen the legal and other documents in the home information pack.

The conveyancer should investigate the issues below:

Drainage	The property has a shared private drainage system situated within the boundaries.
Planning and any other permission needed	The property has been altered by the construction of a side extension which may have required statutory consents.
Boundaries (including Party Walls)	The left hand boundary where this adjoins the road is undefined.
Easements	Above ground cables cross the site and these are not for the sole benefit of the subject property.
Previous structural repairs New building warranties Building insurance (ongoing claims)	I understand that certain works including structural strengthening, and timber and damp treatment have been carried out to parts of the property.
Tree preservation orders	I understand that certain trees within the boundaries to the property are affected by Tree Preservation Orders.

DANGEROUS MATERIALS AND CONTAMINATED LAND, SUBSIDENCE AND FLOODING

The home inspector assumes that:

- The home is not built with nor contains hazardous materials; and it is not built on contaminated land. However, if any of these materials are found during the inspection, or if the home inspector finds evidence to suspect that the land may be contaminated, this will be shown on the report along with recommendations for further investigations.

HEALTH AND SAFETY RISKS

The home inspector will draw your attention to items from a set list of health and safety issues if they are seen at the property.

The inspector does not have to identify risks which have existed in the property for a long time, and which cannot reasonably be changed. As an example, the inspector will not draw your attention to uneven floor surfaces that have existed for decades.

> - The lack of windows that are easy to escape from at first floor level increases the risk of being trapped in the event of fire.
> - The lack of fire doors between the lounge and kitchen increases the risk of being trapped in the event of fire.
> - The home is in an area where high levels of naturally occurring radon gas are emitted from the ground. Take the advice of the NRPB (National Radiological Protection Board).

SECTION D

OUTSIDE CONDITION

The inspector carried out a non-invasive inspection of the outside of the main building and permanent outbuildings. They made this inspection from various points within the boundaries of the property and from public areas such as footpaths and open spaces, using binoculars where necessary. The inspector did not stand on walls or enter neighbouring private property. They examined roofs, chimneys and other external surfaces of the building from the ground. They inspected flat roofs to single-storey buildings from a ladder, where the surface of the roof was not more than three-metres above ground level. They did not inspect features above this level that cannot be seen from any point. Because of the risk of causing damage, the inspector did not walk on flat roofs. They assessed rainwater fittings (gutters and downpipes) only if there was heavy rain at the time of inspection.

The inspector looked at the overall condition and the state of repair of the outside parts of the property. The report does not reflect every minor blemish and does not point out each individual minor defect in the outside walls. However, where there are so many minor defects that together they are serious, the report will say this.

FLATS: OUTSIDE INSPECTION

When inspecting blocks of flats, it is often difficult to see the whole outside of a building or block, and its maintenance is rarely the responsibility of one person. The inspector only carried out a non-invasive inspection to the level of detail set out above, to the main walls, windows and roof over the flat.

The inspector did not inspect the rest of the block to this level of detail; but instead has formed an opinion based on a general inspection of the rest of the block. They provide information about the outside and shared parts so that the conveyancer can check whether the maintenance clauses in the lease or other title documents are adequate.

The inspector inspected the shared access to the flat together with the area where car parking and any garage for the flat are, along with the access to that area. They did not inspect other shared parts, such as separate halls, stairs and access ways to other flats in the block, the lift motor room and cleaning cupboards.

> I could not inspect the surfaces of the flat roofs and some of the pitched roof surfaces because they were concealed by moss growth. I could not inspect the left hand wall because it was concealed by shrub and plant growth.

D1 CHIMNEY STACKS	
Identifying name for the part (where more than one is recorded.)	A) Front chimney stack B) Rear chimney stack
Condition Rating	A) Front chimney stack – 2 B) Rear chimney stack – 1
Justification for Rating and Comments	The chimney stacks are of brick. The brickwork and cementwork to the front stack is cracked and eroded. This requires repair or replacement, but is not considered serious or urgent.

SECTION D (continued)

D2 ROOF COVERINGS	
Identifying name for the part (where more than one is recorded.)	A) Sloping roofs B) Flat dormer roofs
Condition Rating	A) 2 B) 2
Justification for Rating and Comments	The main and back addition roofs are sloping and covered with hand-made clay peg tiles. The tiles in places are poorly secured, have slipped, lifted or have become eroded and damaged or are missing. Areas of the roof are moss covered. The underfelt to the sloping roofs, in particular to the rear part of the house is torn. The felted flat roof areas are inadequately sloped, holding water and are moss covered. This requires repair or replacement, but is not considered serious or urgent.

D3 RAIN WATER PIPES & GUTTERS	
Identifying name for the part (where more than one is recorded.)	
Condition Rating	2
Justification for Rating and Comments	The rainwater fittings are of plastic. The gutters and gullies have become blocked and obstructed with moss and debris. The gutters are out of alignment. The gutter joints, in particular to the rear elevation are damaged. This requires repair or replacement, but is not considered serious or urgent.

SECTION D (continued)

D4 MAIN WALLS & CLADDINGS	
Identifying name for the part (where more than one is recorded.)	A) Original building B) Side extension C) Damp proof course
Condition Rating	A) Original building – 2 B) Side extension – 1 C) Damp proof course – 1
Justification for Rating and Comments	The walls to the original building are 300-350mm thick and are of solid construction, mainly brick, with 150mm timber framed projections forming the dormers to the roof. The bases of some walls are rendered and painted. The walls to the rear extension are of 300mm thick cavity construction. There are brick parapets adjacent to the main and extension roofs. A) The pointing to the original building, in particular around the gulley is loose and eroded. The parapets are eroded. This requires repair or replacement, but is not considered serious or urgent. B) No repair is presently required. Normal maintenance must be undertaken. C) The damp proof course, in particular to the left hand side elevation is bridged by high external ground levels. No repair is presently required, but normal maintenance must be undertaken.

D5 WINDOWS	
Identifying name for the part (where more than one is recorded.)	–
Condition Rating	2
Justification for Rating and Comments	The windows are single-glazed timber casement. The windows, in particular to the front elevation are rotten. The window to the kitchen will not open. The remaining windows are draughty and poorly installed. This requires repair or replacement, but is not considered serious or urgent.

D6 EXTERNAL DOORS	
Identifying name for the part (where more than one is recorded.)	–
Condition Rating	2
Justification for Rating and Comments	The external doors are part-glazed and panelled timber. The rear door is swollen and difficult to open. The rear door is rotten. This requires repair or replacement, but is not considered serious or urgent.

SECTION D (continued)

D7 ALL OTHER WOODWORK	
Identifying name for the part (where more than one is recorded.)	–
Condition Rating	2
Justification for Rating and Comments	The roof rafter feet are exposed at the eaves. The timberwork is wood beetle damaged and stained. This requires repair or replacement, but is not considered serious or urgent.

D8 OUTSIDE DECORATION	
Identifying name for the part (where more than one is recorded.)	–
Condition Rating	2
Justification for Rating and Comments	Decorated areas include the exterior doors, windows and rendered wall plinths. The decorations are incomplete, faded, peeling and blistered, resulting in rot, in particular to the windows. This requires repair or replacement, but is not considered serious or urgent.

D9 OTHER OUTSIDE DETAIL	
Identifying name for the part (where more than one is recorded.)	There are no other external details.
Condition Rating	–
Justification for Rating and Comments	–

SECTION E

INSIDE CONDITION

The home inspector carried out a non-invasive inspection of all the parts of the home they could see without causing damage. However, if the inspector could not see a part of the home without the risk of damage, and they suspect that there could be a problem, the report will say this and include recommendations on the need for further investigation.

The home inspector checked for damp in vulnerable areas by using a moisture-measuring meter.

They inspected the roof structure from inside the roof space where it was accessible but did not move or lift insulation material, stored goods and other contents. The inspector did not walk around the space if there was a risk to safety (for example, where insulation covers the ceiling joists); instead they inspected the roof from the access point.

They opened some of the windows and all the doors, they inspected floor surfaces and under-floor spaces where they were readily accessible, they did not move or lift furniture, floor coverings or other contents. The home inspector has not commented on sound insulation or chimney flues (or both), because it is rarely practical to do so without using specialist equipment that home inspectors do not carry.

I could not inspect the first floor front bedroom because the door giving access was locked. I could not inspect the understairs cupboard because the area was filled with stored items.

E1 ROOF STRUCTURE	
Identifying name for the part (where more than one is recorded.)	A) Roof structure B) Roof space
Condition Rating	A) Roof structure – 2 B) Roof space – 2
Justification for Rating and Comments	The main roof frame is constructed of cut softwood timber. A) The roof timbers are distorted, stained, split and infested by wood boring beetle. This requires repair or replacement, but is not considered serious or urgent. B) The roof space is infested by vermin. This requires repair or replacement, but is not considered serious or urgent.

E2 CEILINGS	
Identifying name for the part (where more than one is recorded.)	–
Condition Rating	2
Justification for Rating and Comments	The ceilings are a mixture of wattle and daub, lath and plaster, plasterboard and fibreboard. There are some exposed timber beams. The ceilings are distorted and affected by cracking. The lath and plaster ceilings are generally uneven. The ceiling in the small rear bedroom is damaged and unstable. This requires repair or replacement, but is not considered serious or urgent.

SECTION E (continued)

E3 INTERNAL WALLS, PARTITIONS & PLASTERWORK	
Identifying name for the part (where more than one is recorded.)	–
Condition Rating	2
Justification for Rating and Comments	The internal walls and partitions are a mixture of solid and lightweight timber construction, most of which is lath and plaster, or plasterboard faced. There are some exposed timber beams. The internal walls are affected by cracking. The plaster is hollow and uneven. The timber vertical cladding in the first floor bathroom is damaged. This requires repair or replacement, but is not considered serious or urgent.

E4 FLOORS	
Identifying name for the part (where more than one is recorded.)	–
Condition Rating	2
Justification for Rating and Comments	The floors are a mixture of suspended timber and solid construction. The timber floors, in particular to the living room are springy, uneven and affected by wood boring beetle. The floor, in particular to the living room is inadequately ventilated. This requires repair or replacement, but is not considered serious or urgent.

E5 FIREPLACES & CHIMNEY BREASTS (AND THE OUTSIDE OF FLUES)	
Identifying name for the part (where more than one is recorded.)	–
Condition Rating	2
Justification for Rating and Comments	The chimney breasts are of mainly brick construction, partly unfinished and partly with a plaster finish. The fireplace openings in the front right hand and rear right hand bedrooms are blocked and are inadequately ventilated. This requires repair or replacement, but is not considered serious or urgent.

E6 BUILT-IN FITTINGS	
Identifying name for the part (where more than one is recorded.)	–
Condition Rating	1
Justification for Rating and Comments	The built-in fittings including kitchen fitments and wardrobes are a mixture of softwood and medium density fibreboard (commonly known as MDF). The kitchen fitments are stained. No repair is presently required, but normal maintenance must be undertaken.

SECTION E (continued)

E7 INSIDE WOODWORK (STAIRCASE, JOINERY, ETC.)	
Identifying name for the part (where more than one is recorded.)	–
Condition Rating	2
Justification for Rating and Comments	The internal woodwork, including doors, skirtings, bannisters and staircases are of mainly painted softwood construction. Skirtings, in particular in the study are partly missing. Skirtings in the living room are affected by rot. This requires repair or replacement, but is not considered serious or urgent.

E8 BATHROOM FITTINGS	
Identifying name for the part (where more than one is recorded.)	–
Condition Rating	1
Justification for Rating and Comments	The sanitary fittings in the bathroom comprise an acrylic panelled bath, low level close-coupled ceramic WC and ceramic wash hand basin. No repair is presently required, but normal maintenance must be undertaken.

E9 DAMPNESS	
Identifying name for the part (where more than one is recorded.)	–
Condition Rating	1
Justification for Rating and Comments	There is evidence of a chemical injection damp proof course to the front, rear and back addition walls. There is no evidence of dampness.

E10 OTHER ISSUES	
Identifying name for the part (where more than one is recorded.)	There are no other internal issues.
Condition Rating	–
Justification for Rating and Comments	–

SECTION F

SERVICES

Services are generally hidden within the construction of the property; for example, pipes are beneath the floors and wiring is within the walls. As a result only the visible parts of the available services can be inspected. Specialist tests were not carried out. The visual inspection does not assess the services to make sure they work properly and efficiently and meet modern standards. If any services (such as the boiler or mains water) are turned off, the home inspector will state that in the report and will not turn them on.

Otherwise, the home inspector turned on some taps on appliances and, where safe and practical to do so, lifted the covers on the drainage inspection chambers. The home inspector reports only on the services covered in this section (electricity, gas, oil, water, heating and drainage). All other services and domestic appliances are not included in the reporting: for example, security and door-answering systems, smoke alarms, television, cable, wireless and satellite communication systems, cookers, hobs, washing machines and fridges (even where built-in). The report gives some general advice on safety and the importance of maintaining the services in the home.

F1 ELECTRICITY	
General Advice endorsed by the Institute of Electrical Engineers	*Safety Warning: Periodic inspection and testing of electrical installations is important to protect your home from damage and to ensure the safety of the occupants. Guidance published by the Institute of Electrical Engineers recommends that inspections and testing are undertaken at least every 10 years and on change of occupancy.* *All electrical installation work undertaken after 1st January 2005 should be identified by an Electrical Installation Certificate.*
Condition Rating	1
Justification for Rating and Comments	There is a mains electricity supply and the meter is located in the understairs cupboard. No repair is presently required, but normal maintenance must be undertaken.

F2 GAS/OIL	
General Advice endorsed by CORGI (Council of Registered Gas Installers)	*Safety Warning: Regular servicing of the gas installation and all gas appliances is important to ensure you protect your home from damage and to ensure the safety of the occupants. This MUST be carried out by a CORGI registered installer. If there is no current certificate relating to an appliance installation, a CORGI registered installer should check and test the installation.*
General Advice endorsed by OFTEC (Oil Firing Technical Association)	*Safety Warning: Periodic inspection and testing of equipment connected with oil installations is important to protect your home and environment and to reduce risks from fire, carbon monoxide poisoning and pollution from leaks. Full advice can be obtained from OFTEC.*
Condition Rating	1
Justification for Rating and Comments	There is a private oil supply with a plastic external storage tank located alongside the garage. No repair is presently required, but normal maintenance must be undertaken.

SECTION F (continued)

F3 WATER	
Condition Rating	1
Justification for Rating and Comments	The water pipe work is copper and the stopcock is in the kitchen. No repair is presently required, but normal maintenance must be undertaken.

F4 HEATING	
Condition Rating	1
Justification for Rating and Comments	Heating is provided by an oil fired, floor standing, open flue boiler located in the kitchen. Hot water is provided by an electric immersion heater. No repair is presently required, but normal maintenance must be undertaken.

F5 DRAINAGE	
Condition Rating	1
Justification for Rating and Comments	There is a private drainage system. Surface water is combined with the foul drainage system. The pitchfibre pipe work is of poor quality. No repair is presently required, but normal maintenance must be undertaken.

SECTION G

GROUNDS

The home inspector inspected the condition of the boundary walls, outbuildings and shared facilities.

To inspect these areas the home inspector walked around the grounds. The report provides a summary of the general condition of any garden walls, fences, and permanent outbuildings. Conservatories with translucent or clear roofs attached to the main buildings are treated as outbuildings, as are garages and permanent store sheds. Buildings containing swimming pools and sports facilities are also treated as outbuildings, but the home inspector does not report on the leisure facilities, such as the pool itself and its equipment.

The inspector did not inspect leisure facilities, landscaping and other facilities, including swimming pools and tennis courts, and non-permanent outbuildings.

There is a double detached garage of brick construction under a felt flat roof. The garage is in a generally fair condition, but some works of repair and maintenance are required. In particular, the building has been affected by longstanding structural movement and the front doors are damaged. No repair is presently required, but normal maintenance must be undertaken.

The boundary walls at the rear are of brick construction. This requires repair or replacement, but is not considered serious or urgent.

Pavings are uneven and breaking up in places. The crazy paved areas alongside the rear main wall of the house are inadequately drained.

The external stairways are affected by longstanding structural movement.

SECTION H

ENERGY PERFORMANCE CERTIFICATE

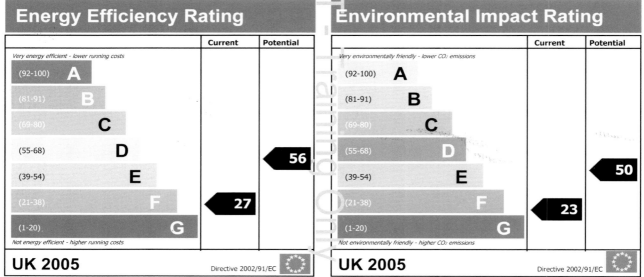

Section H: Energy Performance Certificate
Save money, improve comfort and help the environment

The following report is based on an inspection carried out for:

Address:	Building type:	Home	Certif. Number:
Period Cottage,	Whole or part:	Whole	Date issued:
The Swim,	Methodology:	RDSAP	Inspector name:
Pikeshire, MM1 1MN	Inspection date:	6/12/2005	

This home's performance ratings

This home has been inspected and its performance rated in terms of its energy efficiency and environmental impact. This is calculated using the UK Standard Assessment Procedure (SAP) for dwellings which gives you an energy efficiency rating based on fuel cost and an environmental impact rating based on carbon dioxide (CO_2) emissions.

Energy Efficiency Rating

	Current	Potential
Very energy efficient - lower running costs		
(92-100) **A**		
(81-91) **B**		
(69-80) **C**		
(55-68) **D**		56
(39-54) **E**		
(21-38) **F**	27	
(1-20) **G**		
Not energy efficient - higher running costs		

UK 2005 Directive 2002/91/EC

The energy efficiency rating is a measure of the overall efficiency of a home. The higher the rating the more energy efficient the home is and the lower the fuel bills will be.

Environmental Impact Rating

	Current	Potential
Very environmentally friendly - lower CO_2 emissions		
(92-100) **A**		
(81-91) **B**		
(69-80) **C**		
(55-68) **D**		
(39-54) **E**		50
(21-38) **F**	23	
(1-20) **G**		
Not environmentally friendly - higher CO_2 emissions		

UK 2005 Directive 2002/91/EC

The environmental impact rating is a measure of this home's impact on the environment. The higher the rating the less impact it has on the environment.

Typical fuel costs and carbon dioxide (CO_2) emissions of this home

This table provides you with an indication of how much it will cost to provide lighting, heating and hot water to this home. The fuel costs and carbon dioxide emissions are calculated based on a SAP assessment of the actual energy use that would be needed to deliver the defined level of comfort in this home, using standard occupancy assumptions, which are described on page 4. The energy use includes the energy used in producing and delivering the fuels to this home. The fuel costs only take into account the cost of fuel and not any associated service, maintenance or safety inspection costs. The costs have been provided for guidance only as it is unlikely they will match actual costs for any particular household.

	Current	Potential
Energy use	83,034 kWh/m2 per year	42,385 kWh/m2 per year
Carbon dioxide emissions	21.8 tonnes per year	11.3 tonnes per year
Lighting	£165 per year	£144 per year
Heating	£1,460 per year	£685 per year
Hot water	£237 per year	£150 per year

To see how this home's performance ratings can be improved please go to page 2

Section H: Energy Performance Certificate

Summary of this home's energy performance related features

The table shows the current performance of each element of this home on the following scale:
Extremely poor/ Very poor/ Poor/ Average/ Good/ Very good/ Excellent

Element	Description	Current performance
Main walls	SO Solid Brick:, Insulation: U Unknown, Solid U: 2.10	???
Main roof	P Pitched, Insulation at: J Joists, Thickness: N None	???
Main floor	U: 1.48 A: 120.80 m2	???
Windows	N Normal, Doble Glazed: 0%	???
Main heating	ADB	???
Main heating controls	CBA No stat control of room temp	???
Secondary heating	JAA Efficiency: 50.00%	???
Hot water	HWP From the primary heating system	???
Lighting	Rooms: 9, L.E.L. Fittings: 0, External lights: None	???

Current energy efficiency rating	F 27
Current environmental impact rating	F 23

Measures to improve this home's performance ratings

The improved energy ratings are cumulative, that is they assume the improvements have been installed in the order that they appear in the table.

Lower cost measures	Typical savings	Energy rating after improvement
Hot water tank, make up to 100mm (4 inches) Jacket	£33	F 28
Draughtproof all doors and windows	£40	F 29
Install cavity wall insulation	£32	F 30
Solid wall add 50mm (2 inches) insulation	£383	E 41
Sub Total	£488	
Higher cost measures		
Fit programmer, roomstat and thermostatic radiator valves	£138	E 46
Replace boiler with fully controlled oil condensing boiler for heating and hot water	£165	E 53
Sub Total	£303	

Potential energy efficiency rating	D 56
Potential environmental impact rating	E 50

Further measures to achieve even higher standards

Double glaze the single glazed windows	£50	D 55
Install solar panel (3 m2)	£70	D 56

Enhanced energy efficiency rating	D 56
Enhanced environmental impact rating	D 65

Improvements to the energy efficiency and environmental impact ratings will usually be in step with each other. However, they can sometimes diverge because reduced energy costs are very occasionally not accompanied by reduced carbon dioxide emissions.

Section H: Energy Performance Certificate

Measures to reduce the running costs and improve this home's energy ratings

Lower cost measures (typically up to £500 each)

These improvements are relatively cheap to install and will be worth tackling first.

Measure 1
Cavity wall

The external walls of your home are built with a gap, called a cavity, between the inside and outside layers of the wall. Cavity wall insulation fills this gap with an insulating material. The material is pumped into the gap through small holes, which are drilled into the outside layer of the walls (the small holes are sealed up afterwards). Because this involves using specialist machinery, a professional installation company must carry out the work. The contractor will thoroughly survey your walls before commencing work to be sure that this type of insulation is right for your home, and provide a guarantee for the work.

Measure 2
Topping up loft insulation

The anticipated cost is based upon a contractor installing an additional 100mm of glass fibre or mineral wool insulation in your loft, but it can also be installed by a capable DIY enthusiast. If you choose a DIY installation then take care not to block ventilation at the edge of the loft space as this may cause condensation. When handling the insulation always wear gloves and a mask.

Measure 3
Hot water and pipe insulation

Improving the insulation of your hot water tank using a very thick jacket will help reduce your heating bills. You should also insulate the hot water pipe connections to the cylinder, for about a metre, or as far as you can get access to them. Fit the jacket over the top of any existing jacket and over any thermostat clamped to the cylinder.

Higher cost measures (typically up to £3000 each)

Measure 4
Condensing boiler

This improvement is most appropriate when your existing central heating boiler needs repair or replacement. A condensing boiler is capable of much higher efficiencies than other types of boiler, meaning it will burn less fuel to heat your property. Only a qualified heating engineer should carry out the installation. [Building Regulations apply to this work, so you should get advice from your local Building Control Authority].

Measure 5
Installation of full controls package

Although your heating sytem already has a room thermostat, you can save more money by adding thermostatic radiator valves as well. They allow you to control the temperature of each room to suit your needs, adding to comfort and reducing your bills. For example, you can set them to be warmer in your living room and bathroom than in your bedrooms. You will need a plumber to fit them to every radiator except one - the radiator in the same room as your room thermostat. You still need the room thermostat, because without it, even when the TRVs have turned off the radiators, the boiler is still burning fuel and wasting your money - so don't let the plumber remove it.

Further measures to achieve an even higher standard

These measures should be considered if aiming for the highest possible standard for this home.

Measure 6
Double glazing

Replacing the existing single glazed windows with double-glazing will improve your comfort in your home by reducing draughts and cold spots near windows. This will also help to save on your heating bills during the long winter months. Building Regulations apply to this work, so you should either use a contractor who is registered with Fensa or get advice from your local Building Control Authority.

Measure 7
Solar water heating

Energy from the sun can be harnessed to provide domestic hot water. These systems do not generally provide space heating, and are described as 'Solar Thermal' systems. They are among the most cost effective renewable energy systems that can be installed on dwellings in urban or rural environments.

Section H: Energy Performance Certificate

About this energy inspection

Energy inspections are not new. They have been available in the UK since the late 1980's. Your inspection has been undertaken by a qualified inspector who has been trained to collect the correct information about the energy efficiency of your home. This information has been processed by a Government approved organisation to produce the energy rating and suggestions in the report. Both the inspector and the energy report supplier are regularly monitored to show that their work is up to standard.

If you would like clarification of the technical information in this energy report please contact the:

Inspector Stuart Fairlie on 01788 833 386

Inspector Registration Number   1000-0009

About this home's performance ratings

The ratings provide you with a measure of the overall energy efficiency of this home and its environmental impact. Both are calculated using the Standard Assessment Procedure (SAP), which is the Government's recommended system of assessing the energy efficiency of dwellings. The ratings take into account the home's insulation, heating systems, hot water system, fixed lighting, ventilation, number of windows and related fuels.

Not all of us use our homes in the same way so to allow one home to be directly compared to another, energy ratings are calculated using 'standard occupancy' assumptions. Standard occupancy assumes that the house is heated for 9 hours a day during weekdays and 16 hours a day at weekends, with the living room heated to 21°C and the rest of the house at 18°C.

The ratings are expressed on a scale of 1 to 100. The higher the energy efficiency rating the more energy efficient the home and the higher the environmental impact rating the less impact it has on the environment.

Homes which are more energy efficient use less energy, saving money and helping to protect the environment. A home with an energy efficiency rating of 100 would be energy self sufficient and so the cost of providing lighting, heating and hot water would be practically zero.

The potential rating shown on page one is the economic potential of the home assuming all cost effective measures have been installed. A home built to the 2005 Building Regulations would typically be at the boundary of bands B and C.

This home's impact on the environment

Carbon dioxide is one of the biggest contributors to the man-made greenhouse effect. The energy we use to heat, light and power our homes produces 28 per cent of the UK's CO_2 emissions.

The average household in the UK creates about six tonnes of CO_2 every year. There are simple steps you can take to cut CO_2 emissions and help prevent climate change. Making your home more energy efficient by adopting the suggestions in this report can help protect the environment by saving CO_2. You could save even more CO_2 by switching to renewable energy sources.

What can I do today?

In addition to the specific measures suggested in this report, don't forget there are many simple measures you can put into action today that will save you money and help reduce your impact on the environment.

For example:

- Check that your heating system thermostat is not set too high (21°C in the living room is suggested)
- Make sure your hot water is not too hot (60°C is suggested)
- Turn off your lights and domestic appliances when not needed, and do not leave TVs and videos on standby
- Do not overfill kettles and saucepans, and use a lid where possible
- Buy energy saving recommended appliances
- Find out if you are eligible for grants or offers to help with the cost of energy saving measures by visiting **www.est.org.uk/myhome** or calling **0800 512 012**.

Appendix A – Glossary

ABBE – Awarding Body for the Built Environment
ABE – Association of Building Engineers
ABI – Association of British Insurers
ACE – Association of Consulting Engineers
ACES – Association of Chief Estate Surveyors and Property Managers in Local Government
acm – asbestos containing material
avm – automated valuation model
BBA – British Board of Agrément
BCIS – Building Cost Information Service
BGS – British Geological Survey
BIAT – British Institute of Architectural Technologists
BISF – British Iron and Steel Federation (now the UK Steel Association)
BRE – Building Research Establishment
BSI – British Standards Institution
BSRIA – Building Services Research and Information Association
BWPDA – British Wood Preserving and Damp Proofing Association
CDM – Construction (Design and Management)
CIBSE – Chartered Institution of Building Services Engineers
CIEH – Chartered Institute of Environmental Health
CIH – Chartered Institute of Housing
CIOB – Chartered Institute of Building
CML – Council of Mortgage Lenders
CORGI – Council for Registered Gas Installers
CPD – Continuing Professional Development
dpc – damp-proof course
dpm – damp-proof membrane
EA – The Environment Agency
EMF – Electromagnetic fields
EPC – Energy Performance Certificate
FAERO – Federation of Authorised Energy Rating Organisations
FENSA – Fenestration Self-Assessment Scheme (set up by the GGF)
FTA – Forestry and Timber Association
GGF – Glass and Glazing Federation
HCR – Home Condition Report
HI – Home Inspector
HICB – Home Inspector Certification Board
HIIRR – Home Inspector Inspection and Reporting Requirements

HIP – Home Information Pack
HSE – Health and Safety Executive
HSV – Homebuyer Survey and Valuation
IEE – Institution of Electrical Engineers
IMBM – Institute of Maintenance and Building Management
ICE – Institution of Civil Engineers
ICES – Institution of Civil Engineering Surveyors
ICW – Institute of Clerks of Works
IRTS – Institute of Remedial Treatment Surveyors
ISA – Independent Surveyors Association
IStructE – Institution of Structural Engineers
LDAI – Lead Development Association International
LLL – life-long learning
MCB – miniature circuit breaker
NAEA – National Association of Estate Agents
NHBC – National House-Building Council
NICEIC – National Inspection Council for Electrical Installation Contracting
NLIS – National Land Information Service
NOS – National Occupational Standards
NQF – National Qualification Framework
NRPB – The National Radiological Protection Board
NVQ – National Vocational Qualification
ODPM – Office of the Deputy Prime Minister
OFT – Office of Fair Trading
OFTEC – Oil Firing Technical Association
prc – prefabricated reinforced concrete
RCD – residual current device
RDS – Remedial Treatment Surveys
RdSAP – Reduced Data Standard Assessment Procedure
RIBA – Royal Institute of British Architects
RICS – Royal Institution of Chartered Surveyors
SAP – Standard Assessment Procedure
SAVA – Surveyors and Valuers Accreditation
SPAB – Society for the Protection of Ancient Buildings
SEDBUK – Seasonal Efficiency of Domestic Boilers in the UK
SPI – Structured Professional Interview
TCPA – Town and Country Planning Association
URRN – Unique Report Reference Number
VRQ – Vocationally Related Qualification

Appendix B – Extract from Home Inspector Inspection and Reporting Requirements

...

1.5.1 Instructions

1.5.1   When receiving instructions, Home Inspectors must first obtain sufficient and relevant information to ensure that the property falls within the scope of Home Information Pack legislation, in order that the instructions can, if necessary, be declined with a minimum of delay [**NOS 1.1.2 & 3.2.3**].

1.5.2   Home Inspectors must know their limitations, particularly in regard to the types of property that fall outside their experience and competence. Instructions outside this expertise must be declined [**NOS 1.1.2, 3.2.2 & 3.2.4**].

1.5.3   Home Inspectors must be completely familiar with the format, terms of engagement and explanatory text of the HCR, and be prepared to explain any sections or terms to the seller before, during and after the inspection [**NOS 3.1.2 & 3.1.4**].

1.5.4   Home Inspectors must set aside sufficient time for the inspection [**NOS 1.2.4**].

1.5.5   Any circumstance that might lead to an actual or perceived conflict of interest must be explored with the seller and/or the person from whom instructions are received [**NOS 1.4.6**]. (Detailed guidance on conflicts of interest is issued from time to time.)

1.5.6   Home Inspectors must identify and disclose any financial relationship/s with other professionals involved in the transaction.

1.5.7   A statement about relationships appears in the printed report. This must be completed, if appropriate. (If no statement is inserted, the software will automatically disregard the entry and go onto the next field in the HCR.)

1.6 Confirming instructions [NOS 3.1.6]

1.6.1   The software will prevent the HCR being issued if instructions have not been confirmed in writing. A transcript of the terms under which the HCR is provided must be included with the Confirmation of Instructions letter.

1.6.2   Home Inspectors must include any specific arrangements that apply to the inspection as revealed in prior conversation/s with the seller, e.g. reference to key access and/or alarms for unaccompanied inspections [**NOS 3.1.8**].

1.7 Preparing for the inspection [NOS 3.2]

1.7.1   Home Inspectors must use any local knowledge to complete the HCR [**NOS 3.2.1 & 3.2.2**], e.g. susceptibility to flooding. Appropriate checks must also be undertaken in the event that Home Inspectors do not have such knowledge in the area.

1.7.2   Home Inspectors must check and ensure that they have all the necessary equipment and tools to undertake the inspection in a satisfactory manner [**NOS 1.2.3 & 4.1**].

1.7.3   Home Inspectors must have the essential tools to undertake the inspection.

1.8 Inspection [NOS 4.1]

1.8.1   Home Inspectors must identify themselves to the person at the property at the inspection and show their Scheme Licence ID card [**NOS 4.1.3**].

1.8.2   Home Inspectors must adhere to the description of the inspection found in the terms in the HCR. They must record any restrictions found on site, and report accordingly.

1.8.3   The inspection must not be destructive or invasive (i.e. cause any significant permanent marking, damage, harm or injury to the building fabric), even if the seller gives verbal permission to do so during the inspection.

1.8.4   Where the Home Inspector recommends further investigations which fall outside the terms of engagement of the HCR, further written instructions must be obtained. This work is not covered by the qualification of a Home Inspector.

1.8.5   Where a normal inspection is impractical (e.g. an ill occupant in one room), the Home Inspector must arrange a second inspection. Otherwise, the failure to inspect the room must be stated and the reason given [**NOS 1.2.6; 3.1.3 & 4.1.6**].

1.8.6   The inspection must be conducted only from the property itself and any adjoining public space. Home Inspectors must decline any suggestion from the seller to trespass on neighbouring property.

1.8.7   Home Inspectors must use all suitable vantage points to view as much of the property as possible, without danger or undue difficulty for themselves.

1.8.8   A suitable ladder must be used for the external inspection of flat roofs, and other elements that cannot be observed from the ground, provided the building element to be observed is three metres or less above the position on which the ladder is placed.

1.8.9   If the services are found to be 'turned off' during the inspection, this must be reported in the HCR.

1.8.10 If children or young persons are left in charge of the property, Home Inspectors must postpone the inspection until a responsible adult can be present.

1.8.11 Home Inspectors must not accept any gifts or invitations, which could in any way be interpreted as an attempt to influence their objectivity and decisions [**NOS 1.4.5**].

1.9 Timescales [NOS 1.2]

1.9.1   Home Inspectors must take decisions based on obtaining sufficient information [**NOS 1.2.5**] in order to prepare HCRs that are complete and comprehensive [**NOS 5.1**]. There are no set timescales for inspection or report delivery, but Home Inspectors must be aware of the risks resulting from hastily prepared reports and inadequate inspection and professional reflection [**NOS 1.4.2**].

1.10 Fees

1.10.1 Home Inspectors must agree the amount of fees, method and time of payment and confirm these agreements, in writing, before the inspection. Home Inspectors may charge additional fees, if arranging to return to the property in order to complete the normal inspection, provided that this need is only identified during the inspection. Such additional fees should be set out separately from the agreed fee for the HCR.

1.10.2 If Home Inspectors provide other professional services for the seller (e.g. by way of a further inspection) which go beyond the scope of the HCR, these services are outside the scope of the Home Inspector's qualification and must be invoiced separately.

1.11 Records and files [NOS 4.2]

1.11.1 Home Inspectors must make accurate and legible records of the inspection [**NOS 4.2.1**], which are to be maintained securely for a period not less than fifteen years.

1.11.2 The identification of the construction and materials employed forms the basis for the evaluation and assessment of the building and the Condition Ratings of the building elements. Such descriptions must therefore be included in the site notes [**NOS 4.1.4**].

1.11.3 Records must also be kept of all queries, communications, etc. related to the particular property [**NOS 2.4.6**].

1.12 Security of information [NOS 2.4]

1.12.1 Home Inspectors may come across personal information about the various parties, in particular the owner, occupier/s and seller of the property, which has no relevance to the HCR. Such information must not be recorded in the site notes or divulged to third parties. Home Inspectors must not ignore their common law duties and responsibilities [**NOS 2.4.4**].

1.12.2 Home Inspectors must not use any information about the property in any other context without first obtaining the owner and/or seller's written permission.

1.12.3 Home Inspectors must keep all information records safe and secure [**NOS 2.4.6**].

1.13 Health & Safety risks – the Home Inspector [NOS 2.1 & 2.2]

1.13.1 Home Inspectors must know and comply with the requirements of the Health and Safety at Work Regulations.

1.13.2 When visiting sites where construction works are in progress, Home Inspectors must comply with the site manager's directions regarding the wearing of safety equipment [**NOS 2.1.2**].

1.14 Home Condition Reports

1.14.1 Home Condition Reports must be complete, objective and satisfy relevant codes of practice and standards [**NOS 5.1.3**].

1.14.2 The standard format is compulsory and must not be altered or added to in any way.

1.14.3 The HCR is only concerned with construction, defects and condition of the building elements. Home Inspectors must not give opinions as to the usefulness, marketability or attraction of any parts of the building, accommodation, grounds, etc.

1.14.4 Security measures to reduce the risk of unlawful entry to a property must not be described in the HCR.

1.14.5 The HCR provides a snapshot of the property at the date of the inspection and should not comment on any planned future alterations [**NOS 4.3.3**].
Home Inspectors must have a working knowledge of all Building Regulations and when any particular regulation came into force.

1.14.6 Although the cost of any necessary remedial works and repairs may influence Home Inspectors' decisions as to the appropriate Condition Rating, reporting on cost is outside the scope of the HCR.

1.14.7 Whilst acting as a Home Inspector, they must not act as specialists concerning potentially harmful substances, materials or services. The HCR is not an Asbestos Inspection as defined in the *Control of Asbestos in the Workplace Regulations* 2002 [the CAW Regulations]. Home Inspectors must only report on readily visible asbestos containing materials.

1.14.8 In the case of flats, where the common areas fall under the CAW Regulations, the Home Inspector must assume that there is a 'dutyholder' as defined in the Regulations, and that a Register of Asbestos and effective Management Plan is in place. In the event that this information is not clearly displayed, the Home Inspector must mention the requirement in Conveyance Enquiries.
See further information on 'Asbestos' in Part II.

1.15.1 Excluded types of property

1.15.1 The types of property that are excluded from the HCR may change from time to time under Regulations. The Home Inspectors must keep abreast of legislation and regulations and ensure that the property for which they receive instructions is not excluded [**NOS 3.2.3**] .

1.15.2 Properties that cannot be assessed under the RDSAP methodology must be assessed under an alternative methodology. They are not excluded.

...

1.17 Reinstatement costs for insurance purposes [NOS 5.1.7]

1.17.1 The HCR includes a calculation of the reinstatement cost, which must be produced in accordance with the latest edition of the BCIS Rebuilding Costs Guides (BCIS Guide), BCIS Rebuild Online or another approved system where such guides are appropriate. This information may be in the reporting software or may be obtained from the BCIS (www.bcis.co.uk). The ABI/BCIS consumer information on reinstatement costs must not be used.

1.17.2 For properties where the calculation is outside the scope of the BCIS Guide no figure is to be calculated. Advice must be inserted that specialist advice must be obtained if a reinstatement cost is required.

1.18 Gross external floor area/Gross internal floor area

1.18.1 Home Inspectors must understand and use the RICS Code of Measuring Practice currently in force, appreciating the inclusions, exclusions and the treatment of garages and other outbuildings.

1.18.2 The gross external (gross internal for flats) floor area to be given in the HCR is the 'true' area, before any reductions in extra floors are made as prescribed in the calculation method in the BCIS Guide. All Measurements must be accurately taken and recorded.

1.19 Energy Ratings – Reduced Data SAP [NOS 4.4]

1.19.1 Home Inspectors must note and record the specific data required under the RDSAP methodology in a consistent and methodical manner [**NOS 4.4.3**]. Some of this information will also be part of the general section of the HCR, but Home Inspectors must note the different emphasis and terminology required for the RDSAP.

1.19.2 Home Inspectors must know and report when RDSAP is an inappropriate methodology for the property under inspection, and either use the correct methodology, if appropriately qualified in it, or procure the services of a practitioner who can deliver the correct methodology.

1.20 Enquiries into the completed HCR [NOS 5.2.4]

1.20.1 Home Inspectors must promptly respond to enquiries from potential buyers, but must only provide clarification on the content of the report. Home Inspectors must not give any further detail or advice.

1.20.2 Any enquiries from potential buyers and others must not be divulged to the seller [**NOS 1.1.4 & 1.4.6**].

1.20.3 In respect of the energy performance certificate, Home Inspectors are required to provide clarification of the energy rating and the advice given on the certificate [**NOS 4.4.4**]. They are not required to provide additional advice outside the scope of the energy performance certificate. The certificate refers the reader to other sources of further advice.

1.21 Complaints, claims, etc.

1.21.1 Complaints may be received by the individual Home Inspector or the Home Condition Report Company providing the report.

1.21.2 When a Home Inspector works for a company s/he must immediately inform them of any complaint received.

1.21.3 All Home Inspectors or the companies providing the report must have a written Statement setting out in unambiguous terms and with definable milestones, the procedures that will be followed in the case of a complaint.

1.21.4 The Statement must include all the internal and external processes available to the complainant and be available on request.

1.21.5 The Home Inspectors or the company must abide by the terms of the Statement and use their best endeavours to resolve the complaint.

1.21.6 The minimum requirements for an internal complaints handling process must include:

1.21.7 An oral or written acknowledgement of an initial oral complaint to be sent to the complainant within a defined period of time [say 24 hours of receipt]. The acknowledgement must advise the complainant.

1.21.8   That formal complaints must be put into writing and they can, if they wish, obtain a form to complete offered by The Certification Scheme which has facilities to help with its completion in cases of need.

1.21.9   The name of the 'Complaints Manager' (CM) to which the complaint is to be addressed.

1.21.10 Written acknowledgement of a written complaint to be sent to the complainant within a defined period of time [say 48 hours of receipt]. This acknowledgement must confirm the process (as defined in the statement) to be adopted by the HCRP in an attempt to resolve the complaint.

1.21.11 Written, oral or face to face contact with the complainant by the CM within a defined period of time [say 7 calendar days].

1.21.12 A written report to the complainant setting out the findings of the CM's investigation within a defined period of time [say 21 days from the contact in (c) above].

1.21.13 Where the complainant is dissatisfied with the results of the internal investigation, the HCRP must co-operate with any external mediation or adjudication process approved by the Certification Scheme.

1.21.14 Maintenance of a Complaints Record Log that identifies the details of the complaint, and the outcome.

1.21.15 Reporting to the Quality Assurance Entity under which the HI is managed in the prescribed format.

1.21.16 The receipt of all complaints.

1.21.17 The outcome of all complaints.

PART 2: PRODUCING HOME CONDITION REPORTS – GUIDANCE

This part of the Guidance refers to miscellaneous matters, where Home Inspectors may have doubts as to the meaning of certain terms or issues used when producing Home Condition Reports. In general, it does not have mandatory force.

Where examples are provided, they are for illustrative purposes only and are not intended to be exhaustive or comprehensive.

2.1 Receiving instructions

2.1.1   The HCR is commissioned by, or on behalf of, the seller of the property. In practice, the instructions may be received from a variety of sources, e.g. solicitors, estate agents or Home Information Pack providers.

2.1.2   There are no statutory or certification scheme fee scales, or requirements for time of invoicing, etc. Home Inspectors and HCR Companies are free to agree these matters directly with the seller or other party from whom the instructions are received.

2.1.3   It is not the duty of Home Inspectors to enquire into the legal ownership of the property, or to verify that the person who issued the instructions, and/or who is met at the inspection, has a right to sell.

2.1.4   Home Inspectors may, however, discover discrepancies or mistakes in names and addresses provided, and when this happens, these should be verified and corrected.

2.1.5   When responding to the instruction and arranging the inspection, Home Inspectors and/or HCR Providers should briefly describe the scope, limitations and constraints of the planned inspection. It may be appropriate to inform the seller that it is not necessary for them to clear cupboards, move furniture or roll back carpets in preparation for the inspection.

2.1.6   HCRs do not have a fixed shelf life. Caveat Emptor (buyer beware) is maintained in the home-buying process and it is therefore up to the buyer and/or lender to decide whether they will rely on the HCR particularly if the property has been on the market for a very long time.

2.1.7   Home Inspectors should encourage the seller to be present at the inspection. If the seller is not available to attend the inspection, Home Inspectors must enquire who will meet them on site, and to whom any queries or questions that may arise during the inspection should be directed [**NOS 1.1.2**]. The presence of the seller helps the collection of practical information and aids the resolution of unexpected problems, such as windows that will not close after opening.

...

Appendix C – Condition rating exercise

Based on what has previously been discussed in Chapter Three in relation to the assessment of building elements and assigning them with a condition rating for the Home Condition Report, this section provides a brief illustration of assigning condition ratings to a building element and applying the relevant standardised text.

The table below contains an extract from the ODPM Mandatory and Preferred Text for use within the Home Condition Report and shows the preferred text options to be considered when reporting upon rainwater fittings under element D3 of the Home Condition Report. The three subsequent scenarios show how the standard text could be used to describe and justify a condition rating in the context of rainwater fittings.

D3 RAIN WATER PIPES & GUTTERS

D31 The	/rainwater fittings	/are	/of /a mixture of	/...[Describe]. /and /...[Describe].		
D32	There are no rainwater fittings.					
D33 The	/rainwater fittings /down pipes /gutter/gutters /gulley/gulleys /hopper head /outlets/outlets /joint/joints /seal/seals /...[Describe]	/to the /in particular to the	/...[Describe]	/is /are /has /have	/loose /incomplete /missing /rusted /cracked /broken /eroded /leaning /stained /damaged /poorly secured /obstructed /blocked /causing damp penetration /inadequate /out of alignment /may contain asbestos material /...[Describe].	

1. No repair is presently required. (1)
2. Normal maintenance must be undertaken. (1)
3. No repair is presently required. Normal maintenance must be undertaken. (1)
4. This requires repair or replacement, but is not considered serious or urgent. (2)
5. This is considered serious and in need of urgent repair or replacement. (3)

SCENARIO ONE

Shows concrete 'Finlock' gutters with an asbestos cement down pipe. Inspection has revealed no indication of water seepage or overspillage. The installation is well secured, with appropriate falls, and shows no signs of distress so far as you can judge from your visual inspection.

D3 RAIN WATER PIPES & GUTTERS	
Identifying name for the part (where more than one is recorded.)	–
Condition Rating	1
Justification for Rating and Comments *Finlock gutter and down pipe*	The rainwater fittings are a mixture of concrete and asbestos cement. The down pipe, in particular to the front elevation may contain asbestos material. No repair is presently required. Normal maintenance must be undertaken.

Comment

Concrete gutter systems, whilst commonplace in local authority housing of the 1950s, are now of an obsolete design. Their performance varies according to the quality of original installation and how well they have been maintained. In this case it would be appropriate to include a comment about the asbestos content of the down pipes, but if there is no indication of a defect, a category one condition rating should be applied.

SCENARIO TWO

Shows PVCu gutters on a building constructed in the 1960s, using softwood fascias and asbestos cement soffits. There are signs of minor rainwater seepage from at least one of the gutter joints, but all the down pipes are well secured and the falls are adequate. The rainwater seepage has not caused damp penetration.

D3 RAIN WATER PIPES & GUTTERS	
Identifying name for the part (where more than one is recorded.)	–
Condition Rating	2
Justification for Rating and Comments 1960s PVCu gutter	The rainwater fittings are of plastic. The gutter joints, in particular to the right hand side elevation are damaged. This requires repair or replacement, but is not considered serious or urgent.

Comment

A repair is clearly needed in order to put right the damaged gutter joint, which has probably perished and failed due to age deterioration. Minor water seepage is not causing any major knock-on effect to the building fabric at the present time. Although works are required, the repair does not need to be carried out straight away, and could almost certainly be left for three to six months without becoming substantially worse. A category two condition rating has been applied.

SCENARIO THREE

Shows a badly dislodged section of cast iron gutter alongside an external dormer window projection. The section is hanging precariously just above an external entrance doorway, and the resultant damage has caused substantial overspillage of rainwater. Staining of decorations is showing through internally and in addition, the corresponding internal area is showing high damp meter readings.

D3 RAIN WATER PIPES & GUTTERS	
Identifying name for the part (where more than one is recorded.)	–
Condition Rating	3
Justification for Rating and Comments *Damaged cast iron gutter*	The rainwater fittings are of cast iron. The gutter to the rear dormer window is dislodged, poorly secured and causing damp penetration. This is considered serious and in need of urgent repair or replacement.

Comment

Due to the severity of the damaged gutter, it will naturally fall into a category two or three condition rating, depending upon how far along the seriousness scale it is. In making a decision on relative seriousness, the questions that were encountered previously in Figure 3.3 need to be considered:

- Is the structural integrity of this element sound?
- Does this element perform its intended function?
- Is the risk to health and safety negligible?
- Can the defect be ignored without becoming a lot worse?

As the answer to at least one of the above questions is 'no', it is clear that the element needs to be given a category three condition rating. Additionally, because of the health and safety implications, this element will also need to be included under Section C of the HCR.

Appendix D – HCR inspection checklist and site notes

Address: ....

Property reference no. (If known) .... Home Inspector name: ....

Related parties: .... Potential conflicts of interest? ....

Inspection date: .... Arrival time: .... Departure time: ....

Additional Notes: ....

....

....

....

Risk checklist	Significant hazards (Identified from brief walk around)	Risk level (Low/medium/high)	Action required?
Safe parking			
Weather conditions			
Vacant property			
Safe access			
Animals			
Occupants			
Chemical substances			
Construction/condition			
Voids/holes/traps			
Cellar access			
Loft access			
Services			
Inspection chambers			

VERBAL ENQUIRIES OF: Owner ☐ Occupier ☐ Not Completed ☐

(reason)...

Q. What is the **AGE** of the property?..

Q. What is the **TENURE?** Freehold ☐ Feuhold ☐ Commonhold ☐ Leasehold ☐ yrs unexpired.....................

Ground Rent £................ Service Charge £................ Tenancy information...

Q. Dates of any **PREVIOUS ALTERATIONS, EXTENSIONS or OTHER WORKS?**
(e.g. requiring Building Regulations/Planning Consent/Listed Building/Party Wall Act, etc.)

(Details) ....

Q. HOW LONG has the owner occupied the property?...years

Q. Is the property **LISTED?**............................. If so, what **GRADE?**...

Q. Is the property located within a **CONSERVATION AREA?**...

Q. Has the property or immediate locality been affected by **FLOODING?**   No..........Yes..........

....

Q. Are there any **RIGHTS OF WAY** that affect the property?   No..........Yes..........

(Details) ....

Q. Any **STRUCTURAL REPAIRS** (e.g. underpinning or strengthening)?   No..........Yes..........

(Details) ....

Q. Any **GUARANTEES** or **WARRANTEES?**   No..........Yes..........

Timber Treatment ☐ Damp Proofing ☐ Wall-Ties ☐ Double Glazing ☐ NHBC ☐

Other... Builder...

Q. What **MAINS SERVICES** are connected?   Gas ☐ Electricity ☐ Water ☐ Drainage ☐

Q. Other services?   No..........Yes..........

Q. Boiler age and service history?...

Q. Stopcock location?..

Q. Are the **ROADS**   Made ☐ Adopted ☐ Unmade ☐ Made ☐ Private ☐

Q. Are there any known **DISPUTES** or **RESTRICTIONS** affecting the property?   No........Yes........

....

....

....

Q. Any other issues:

....

....

....

THE PROPERTY INSPECTION

Type: .... Date built: .... Date extended: ....

Details of extension/conversion: ....

Accommodation:

External facilities: ....

Garage/carport: Double/single/space/none

Outbuildings: Outside WC/conservatory/stable/swimming pool/shed/greenhouse/other

....

Siting and risks:

Located in mainly tenanted area? ....

Adverse factors: ....

Access difficulties: ....

Subsoils/gradient/known problems: ....

Flooding: ....

Mining: ....

Contamination/environmental: ....

Legal risks: ....

Circumstances of the inspection:

Weather: Mild ☐ Dry ☐ Hot ☐ Cold ☐ Wet ☐ Drizzle ☐

               Rain ☐ Snow ☐ Windy ☐ Intermittent ☐ Constant ☐...

Floors covered: Part ☐ No ☐ Yes ☐

Property: Occupied ☐ Vacant ☐ Signs of Tenancy ☐ Furnished ☐ Part ☐ Unfurnished ☐

Parts not inspected: ....

....

SITE SKETCH PLAN: Orientation: Front of property faces   N ☐ S ☐ E ☐ W ☐ ....

Key

Airbrick

Boundary

Drain cover

Drain lines

Gulley

Trees

Parapets

Retaining walls

Flues

Roof slopes

Storeys

Insurance reinstatement cost calculation:

Gross external floor area ....(square metres)

M^2 at £ ....   £ ....

Add £ ....

Add £ ....

Add £ ....   Total £ ....

FLOOR PLAN, SKETCHES AND OTHER NOTES

Key

Damp checks

High damp readings

Spirit level checks

Floor slopes

Wall tilt

Carpeted floor

Timber floor

Solid floor

Wall panelled

Wall concealed

SECTION D: OUTSIDE CONDITION

D1 Chimney stacks

Rating: 1 ☐ 2 ☐ 3 ☐ NI ☐ FASBO ☐

FASBO: Further advice should be obtained

D2 Roof coverings

Rating: 1 ☐ 2 ☐ 3 ☐ NI ☐ FASBO ☐

D3 Rain water pipes and gutters

Rating: 1 ☐ 2 ☐ 3 ☐ NI ☐ FASBO ☐

D4 Main walls and claddings

Rating: 1 ☐ 2 ☐ 3 ☐ NI ☐ FASBO ☐

Structural movement

Damp course

Ground levels

Sub floor ventilation

D5 Windows

Rating: 1 ☐ 2 ☐ 3 ☐ NI ☐ FASBO ☐

D6 External doors

Rating: 1 ☐ 2 ☐ 3 ☐ NI ☐ FASBO ☐

D7 All other woodwork

Rating: 1 ☐ 2 ☐ 3 ☐ NI ☐ FASBO ☐

D8 Outside decoration

Rating: 1 ☐ 2 ☐ 3 ☐ NI ☐ FASBO ☐

D9 Other outside detail

Rating: 1 ☐ 2 ☐ 3 ☐ NI ☐ FASBO ☐

SECTION E: INSIDE CONDITION

E1 Roof structure (1)

Rating: 1 ☐ 2 ☐ 3 ☐ NI ☐ FASBO ☐

E1 Roof structure (2)

Rating: 1 ☐ 2 ☐ 3 ☐ NI ☐ FASBO ☐

E2 Ceilings

Rating: 1 ☐ 2 ☐ 3 ☐ NI ☐ FASBO ☐

E3 Internal walls, partitions and plasterwork

Rating: 1 ☐ 2 ☐ 3 ☐ NI ☐ FASBO ☐

E4 Floors

Rating: 1 ☐ 2 ☐ 3 ☐ NI ☐ FASBO ☐

E5 Fireplaces and chimney breasts (and the outside of flues)

Rating: 1 ☐ 2 ☐ 3 ☐ NI ☐ FASBO ☐

E6 Built-in fittings

Rating: 1 ☐ 2 ☐ 3 ☐ NI ☐ FASBO ☐

E7 Inside Woodwork (staircase, joinery, etc.)

Rating: 1 ☐ 2 ☐ 3 ☐ NI ☐ FASBO ☐

E8 Bathroom fittings

Rating: 1 ☐ 2 ☐ 3 ☐ NI ☐ FASBO ☐

E9 Dampness

Rating: 1 ☐ 2 ☐ 3 ☐ NI ☐ FASBO ☐

Rising:

Penetrating:

Condensation:

(Timber defects)

Wood beetle:

Rot:

E10 Other issues

SECTION F: SERVICES

F1 Electricity

Rating: 1 ☐ 2 ☐ 3 ☐ NI ☐ FASBO ☐

F2 Gas/Oil

Rating: 1 ☐ 2 ☐ 3 ☐ NI ☐ FASBO ☐

F3 Water

Rating: 1 ☐ 2 ☐ 3 ☐ NI ☐ FASBO ☐

F4 Heating

Rating: 1 ☐ 2 ☐ 3 ☐ NI ☐ FASBO ☐

F5 Drainage

Rating: 1 ☐ 2 ☐ 3 ☐ NI ☐ FASBO ☐

SECTION G (CONDITION RATINGS NOT REQUIRED)

(Garages, grounds, boundary walls, outbuildings and common facilities, etc.)

Garages

Permanent sheds/outbuildings

Boundary and other walls

Grounds/trees/paved areas

Shared facilities

Detached conservatories/other structures

Health and safety risks (Summary)

Legal/environmental/other risks (Summary)

Rating 3 defects (Summary)

Appendix E – Useful addresses and websites

The information contained in this appendix is correct at the time of going to press.

Awarding Body for the Built Environment (ABBE)
Edge Building
Perry Barr
Birmingham
B42 2SU
Tel: +44 (0)121 331 5174
www.uce.ac.uk/abbe

Asset Skills
6a Christchurch Road
Unit 16, Mobbs Miller House
Abington
Northampton NN1 5LL
Tel: +44 (0)1604 233336
Fax: +44 (0)1604 233573
www.assetskills.org

Association of British Insurers (ABI)
51 Gresham Street
London
EC2V 7HQ
Tel: +44 (0)20 7600 3333
Fax: +44 (0)20 7696 8999
www.abi.org.uk

Association of Building Engineers (ABE)
Lutyens House
Billing Brook Road
Weston Favell
Northampton
NN3 8NW
Tel: +44 (0)1604 404121
Fax: +44 (0)1604 784220
www.abe.org.uk

Association of Chief Estate Surveyors and Property Managers in Local Government (ACES)
23 Athol Road
Bramhall
Cheshire SK7 1BR
Tel: +44 (0)161 439 9589
Fax: +44 (0)161 440 7383
www.aces.org.uk

Association of Consulting Engineers (ACE)
Alliance House
12 Caxton Street
London SW1H 0QL
Tel: +44 (0)20 7222 6557
Fax: +44 (0)20 7222 0750
www.acenet.co.uk

British Board of Agrément (BBA)
PO Box 195
Bucknalls Lane
Garston
Watford
Hertfordshire
WD25 9BA
Tel: +44 (0)1923 665300
Fax: +44 (0)1923 665301
www.bbacerts.co.uk

British Geological Survey (BGS)
Kingsley Dunham Centre
Keyworth
Nottingham
NG12 5GG
Tel: +44 (0)115 936 3100
Fax: +44 (0)115 936 3200
www.bgs.ac.uk, www.bgs.ac.uk/geoindex,
www.bgs.ac.uk/georeports

British Institute of Architectural Technologists (BIAT)
397 City Road
London EC1V 1NH
Tel: +44 (0)20 7278 2206
Fax: +44 (0)20 7837 3194
www.biat.org.uk

British Standards Institution (BSI)
389 Chiswick High Road
London W4 4AL
Tel: +44 (0)20 8996 9000
Fax: +44 (0)20 8996 7001
www.bsi-global.com

Building Services Research and Information Association (BSRIA)
BSRIA Ltd.
Old Bracknell Lane West
Bracknell
Berkshire RG12 7AH
Tel: +44 (0)1344 465600
Fax: +44 (0)1344 465626
www.bsria.co.uk

Building Cost Information Service (BCIS)
3 Cadogan Gate
London SW1X 0AS
Tel: +44 (0)20 7695 1500
Fax: +44 (0)20 7695 1501
www.bcis.co.uk

Building Research Establishment
Bucknalls Lane
Garston
Watford WD25 9XX
Tel: +44 (0)1923 664000
www.bre.co.uk

British Wood Preserving and Damp Proofing Association (BWPDA)
1 Gleneagles House
Vernon Gate
Derby
DE1 1UP
Tel: +44 (0)1332 225100
Fax: +44 (0)1332 225101
www.bwpda.co.uk

Chartered Institute of Environmental Health (CIEH)
Chadwick Court
15 Hatfields,
London SE1 8DJ
Tel: +44 (0)20 7928 6006
Fax: +44 (0)20 7827 5862
www.cieh.org

Chartered Institute of Building (CIOB)
Englemere
Kings Ride
Ascot
Berks SL5 7TB
Tel: +44 (0)1344 630700
Fax: +44 (0)1344 630777
www.ciob.org.uk

Chartered Institute of Housing (CIH)
Octavia House
Westwood Way
Coventry CV4 8JP
Tel: +44 (0)24 7685 1700
Fax: +44 (0)24 7669 5110
www.cih.org

Chartered Institute of Building Services Engineers (CIBSE)
222 Balham High Road
London
SW12 9BS
Tel: +44 (0)20 8675 5211
Fax: +44 (0)20 8675 5449
www.cibse.org

Construction Industry Research and Information Association (CIRIA)
Classic House
174–180 Old Street
London
EC1V 9BP
Tel: +44 (0)20 7549 3300
Fax: +44 (0)20 7253 0523
www.ciria.org.uk

Council of Mortgage Lenders (CML)
3 Savile Row
London
W1S 3PB
Tel: +44 (0)20 7437 0075
www.cml.org.uk

CORGI (The Council for Registered Gas Installers)
1 Elmwood
Chineham Park
Crockford Lane
Basingstoke
Hants
RG24 8WG
Tel: +44 (0)870 401 2200
Fax: +44 (0)870 401 2600
www.corgi-gas-safety.com

Elmhurst Energy Systems Ltd.
Elmhurst Farm
Bow Lane
Withybrook
Coventry
CV7 9LQ
Tel: +44 (0)1788 833386
Fax: +44 (0)1788 832690
www.elmhurstenergy.co.uk

English Heritage
PO Box 569
Swindon
SN2 2YP
Tel: +44 (0)870 333 1181
Fax: +44 (0)1793 414926
www.english-heritage.org.uk

The Environment Agency
For information on regional offices, contact General Enquiries (+44 (0)8708 506 506)or visit www.environment-agency.gov.uk

**Federation of Authorised Energy Rating
Organisations (FAERO)**
For information on FAERO's member organisations,
see entries for Elmhurst Energy Systems Ltd., MVM
Consultants Plc. and National Energy Services

Forestry and Timber Association (FTA)
5 Dublin Street Lane South
Edinburgh
EH1 3PX
Tel: +44 (0)131 538 7111
Fax: +44 (0)131 538 7222
www.forestryandtimber.org

Glass and Glazing Federation (GGF)
44–48 Borough High Street
London
SE1 1XB
Tel: +44 (0)870 042 4255
Fax: +44 (0)870 042 4266
www.ggf.co.uk

Home Inspector Certification Board (HICB)
c/o Property Industry Research Ltd.
PO Box 3546
Ferndown
Dorset
BH22 0XP
Tel: +44 (0)1202 890988
www.hicb.co.uk

Homecheck
Imperial House
21–25 North Street
Bromley
BR1 1SS
Tel: +44 (0)870 606 1700
Fax: +44 (0)870 606 1701
www.homecheck.co.uk

Health and Safety Executive (HSE)
Magdalen House
Trinity Road
Bootle
Merseyside
L20 3QZ
Tel: +44 (0)8701 545 500
www.hse.gov.uk

Institution of Civil Engineers (ICE)
1 Great George Street
London
SW1P 3AA
Tel: +44 (0)20 7222 7722
www.ice.org.uk

Institution of Civil Engineering Surveyors (ICES)
Dominion House
Sibson Road
Sale
Cheshire M33 7PP
Tel: +44 (0)161 972 3100
Fax: +44 (0)161 972 3118
www.ices.org.uk

**Institute of Clerks of Works of Great Britain
Incorporated (ICW)**
Equinox
28 Commerce Road
Lynch Wood
Peterborough
PE2 6LR
Tel: +44 (0)1733 405160
Fax: +44 (0)1733 405161
www.icwgb.org

Institution of Electrical Engineers (IEE)
Savoy Place
London WC2R 0BL
Tel: +44 (0)20 7240 1871
Fax: +44 (0)20 7240 7735
www.iee.org

**Institute of Maintenance and Building
Management (IMBM)**
Keets House
30 East Street
Farnham
Surrey GU9 7SW
Tel: +44 (0)1252 710994
Fax: +44 (0)1252 737741
www.imbm.org.uk

Institute of Remedial Treatment Surveyors (IRTS)
Essex House
High Street
Chipping Ongar
Essex CM5 9EB
Tel: +44 (0)800 915 6363
Fax: +44 (0)870 755 5432
www.irts.co.uk

Independent Surveyors Association (ISA)
Broadbury
Okehampton
Devon EX20 4NH
Tel: +44 (0)1837 871700
www.surveyorsweb.co.uk

Institution of Structural Engineers (IstructE)
11 Upper Belgrave Street
London SW1X 8BH
Tel: +44 (0)20 7235 4535
Fax: +44 (0)20 7235 4294
www.istructe.org.uk

Lead Development Association International (LDAI)
42 Weymouth Street
London W1G 6NP
Tel: +44 (0)20 7499 8422
Fax: +44 (0)20 7493 1555
www.ldaint.org

MVM Consultants
MVM House
2 Oakfield Road
Clifton
Bristol BS8 2AL
Tel: +44 (0)117 9744477
Fax: +44 (0)117 9706897
www.mvm.co.uk

National Association of Estate Agents (NAEA)
Arbon House
21 Jury Street
Warwick CV34 4EH
Tel: +44 (0)1926 496800
www.naea.co.uk

National Energy Services Ltd.
The National Energy Centre
Davy Avenue
Knowlhill
Milton Keynes
MK5 8NA
Tel: +44 (0)1908 672787
Fax: +44 (0)1908 662296
www.nesltd.co.uk

National House Building Council (NHBC)
Buildmark House
Chiltern Avenue
Amersham
Buckinghamshire HP6 5AP
Tel: +44 (0)1494 735363
www.nhbc.co.uk

National Inspection Council for Electrical Installation Contracting (NICEIC)
Vintage House
37 Albert Embankment
London SE1 7UJ
Tel: +44 (0)20 7564 2323
Fax: +44 (0)20 7564 2370
www.niceic.org.uk

National Land Information Service (NLIS)
Local Government Information House
Layden House
76–86 Turnmill Street
London
EC1M 5LG
Tel: +44 (0)870 240 6760
www.nlis.org.uk

National Radiological Protection Board (NRPB)
Chilton
Didcot
Oxon
OX11 0RQ
Tel: +44 (0)1235 831600
Fax: +44 (0)1235 833891
www.nrpb.org

Office of the Deputy Prime Minister (ODPM)
26 Whitehall
London
SW1 2WH
Tel: +44 (0)20 7944 4400
www.odpm.gov.uk

Office of Fair Trading (OFT)
Fleetbank House
2–6 Salisbury Square
London
EC4Y 8JX
Tel: +44 (0)20 7211 8000
Fax: +44 (0)20 7211 8800
www.oft.gov.uk

Oil Firing Technical Association (OFTEC)
Foxwood House
Dobbs Lane
Kesgrave
Ipswich IP5 2QQ
Tel: +44 (0)845 658 5080
Fax: +44 (0)845 658 5181
www.oftec.co.uk

Ordnance Survey
Romsey Road
Southampton
SO16 4GU
Tel: +44 (0)845 605 0505
Fax: +44 (0)238 079 2615
www.ordnancesurvey.co.uk

Qualifications and Curriculum Authority (QCA)
83 Piccadilly
London
W1J 8QA
Tel: +44 (0)20 7509 5555
Fax: +44 (0)20 7509 6666
www.qca.org.uk

Royal Institute of British Architects (RIBA)
66 Portland Place
London
W1B 1AD
Tel: +44 (0)20 7580 5533
www.architecture.com

RICS Books
Surveyor Court
Westwood Way
Coventry
CV4 8JE
Tel: +44 (0)20 7222 7000
(or 0870 333 1600 Contact Centre)
www.ricsbooks.com

Royal Institution of Chartered Surveyors (RICS)
12 Great George Street
London
SW1P 3AD
Tel: +44 (0)20 7222 7000
(or 0870 333 1600 Contact Centre)
www.rics.org

Royal Institution of Chartered Surveyors (Scotland)
9 Manor Place
Edinburgh
EH3 7DN
Tel: +44 (0)131 225 7078
Fax: +44 (0)131 240 0830
www.rics-scotland.org.uk

Surveyors and Valuers Accreditation (SAVA)
PO Box 5603
Milton Keynes
MK5 8XR
Tel: +44 (0)870 837 6565
Fax: +44 (0)870 837 6566
www.sava.org.uk

SEDBUK
(Seasonal Efficiency of Domestic Boilers in the UK)
www.sedbuk.com

Society for the Protection of Ancient Buildings (SPAB)
37 Spital Square
London
E1 6DY
Tel: +44 (0)20 7377 1644
Fax: +44 (0)20 7247 5296
www.spab.org.uk

Soil Association
Bristol House
40–56 Victoria Street
Bristol
BS1 6BY
Tel: +44 (0)117 314 5000
Fax: +44 (0)117 314 5001
www.soilassociation.org

Subsidence Claims Advisory Bureau
Charter House
43 St. Leonards Road
Bexhill-on-Sea
East Sussex TN40 1JA
Tel: +44 (0)1424 733727
Fax: +44 (0)1424 731781
www.subsidencebureau.com

The Suzy Lamplugh Trust
PO Box 17818
London SW14 8WW
Tel: +44 (0)20 8876 0305
Fax: +44 (0)20 8876 0891
www.suzylamplugh.org

Town and Country Planning Association (TCPA)
17 Carlton House Terrace
London SW1Y 5AS
Tel: +44 (0)20 7930 8903
Fax: +44 (0)20 7930 3280
www.tcpa.org.uk

UK legislation
UK legislation from 1988 onward is published on the HMSO website
www.hmso.gov.uk/legislation/about_legislation.htm.
UK legislation prior to 1988 may be purchased through The Stationery Office Limited (TSO).
HMSO legislation enquiries tel: 020 7276 5210

UK Steel Association
Broadway House
Tothill Street
London SW1H 9NQ
Tel: +44 (0)20 7222 7777
Fax: +44 (0)20 7222 2782
www.uksteel.org.uk

Appendix F – Further information

The reforms surrounding the *Housing Act* 2004 are still in the process of development and changes to the detail of some of the proposals will undoubtedly take place before the final stages of implementation. Further information may be found by visiting the following websites:

ODPM page on the Home Information Pack	**www.odpm.gov.uk/index.asp?id=1150984**
ODPM Factsheet 7: *The Home Information Pack*	**www.odpm.gov.uk/index.asp?id=1151011**
Asset Skills	**www.assetskills.org**
RICS HCRwriter	**www.hcrwriter.com**
Property Information Research Ltd	**www.pirltd.org.uk**

BCIS PUBLICATIONS

The following BCIS cost guides are also available from **www.ricsbooks.com** and are reproduced each year with revised data:

BCIS, *Housing Repair Cost Guide*, BCIS Limited, London, 2004

BCIS, *Guide to House Rebuilding Costs 2005*, BCIS Limited, London, 2005

BCIS, *Guide to House Rebuilding Costs Regional Supplement 2005*, BCIS Limited, London, 2005

BCIS, *Guide to Rebuilding Costs of Flats 2005*, BCIS Limited, London, 2005

BCIS Rebuild *Online* (subscription service) **www.bcis.co.uk**

FURTHER READING

Brereton, C., *The Repair of Historic Buildings* (2nd edition), English Heritage, London, 1999 (ISBN 1 85074 527 7)

Burkinshaw, R. and Parrett, M. J., *Diagnosing Damp*, RICS Books, Coventry, 2003 (ISBN 1 84219 097 0)

Dickinson, P. R. and Thornton, N., *Cracking and Building Movement*, RICS Books, Coventry, 2004 (ISBN 1 84219 156 X)

Hollis, M., *Pocket Surveying Buildings*, RICS Books, Coventry, 2002 (ISBN 1 84219 074 1)

Hollis, M., *Surveying Buildings* (5th edition), RICS Books, Coventry, 2005 (ISBN 1 84219 192 6)

isurv Building Surveying, RICS Books, Coventry, 2005 (ISBN 1 84219 190 X)

Parnham, P. and Rispin, C., *Home Inspector's Handbook*, RICS Books, Coventry, 2005 (ISBN 1 84219 203 5)

RICS Asbestos Working Party, *Asbestos and its implications for property professionals*, RICS Books, Coventry, 2003 (ISBN 1 84219 063 6)

RICS Residential Property Faculty, *Building Surveys of Residential Property*, RICS Books, Coventry, 2004 (ISBN 1 84219 095 4)

RICS Property Measurement Group, *Code of Measuring Practice – A Guide for Surveyors and Valuers* (5th Edition), RICS Books, Coventry, 2001 (ISBN 1 84219 609 5)

.

Index